To Nancy,
upon Graduation — June, 1978
From all the wild creatures who love her so
and who — one dark spring evening
Did hear the 'Nightwatcher' Call —
Joy, Spotz, Pete, Sooka and Ms. A. Peabody

THE NIGHTWATCHERS

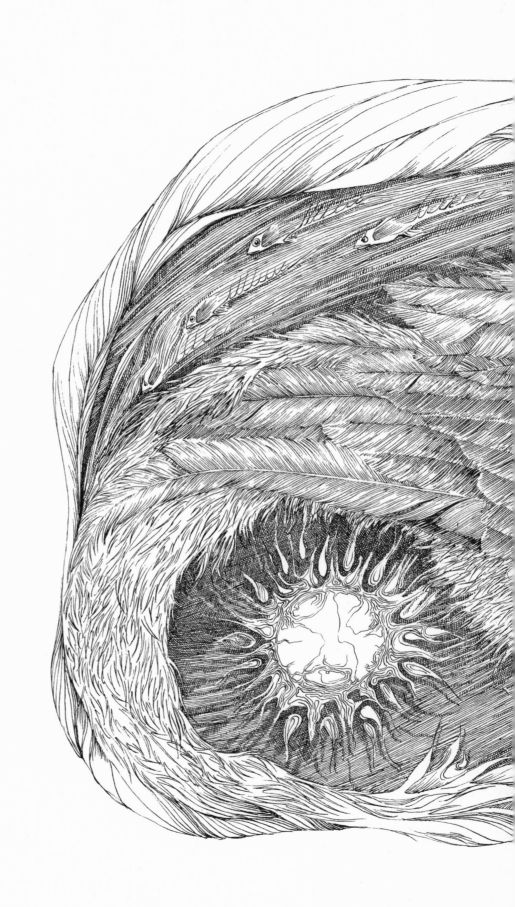

THE
NIGHTWATCHERS

BY ANGUS CAMERON
AND PETER PARNALL

FOUR WINDS PRESS
NEW YORK

Published by Four Winds Press
A Division of Scholastic Magazines, Inc., New York, N.Y.
Copyright © 1971 Peter Parnall & Angus Cameron
All Rights Reserved.
Printed in the United States of America
Library of Congress Catalogue Card Number: 70-161023
Endpaper Drawing by Ginny Parnall
First printing, 1971
Second printing, 1972
Third printing, 1972

CONTENTS

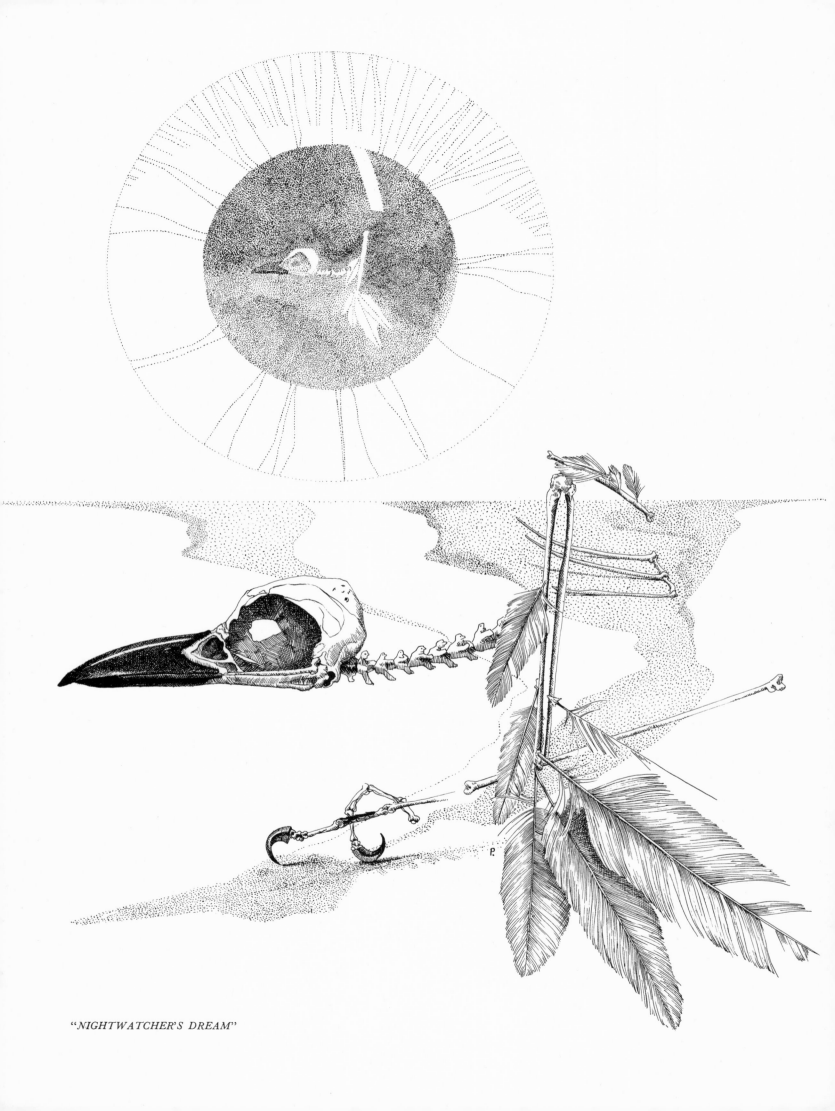

"NIGHTWATCHER'S DREAM"

WHY OWLS?

Many years ago my friend Jean Piatt, now a professor of anatomy at the medical school of the University of Pennsylvania, advised that I ought to specialize my interest in birds. My mentor did not take his own advice for today he (and his wife, Marybelle) is one of the small number of American bird watchers with a "life list" that contains more than 600 of the 700 plus species of North American birds. In any case, it was easy for *me* to take his advice for at that time my interest had already concentrated to a considerable degree on the hawks and owls. That interest has never flagged. Of course, "specialization" for me is a relatively modest thing. I am not an ornithologist; rather I am an enthusiast for the predaceous birds. Being a hunter and fisherman, I consider these birds fellow creatures. A psychiatrist friend tells me that the preference is one of my devices for sublimating my aggressions. Perhaps so. In any case, that's the way it has been with me. During many trips into the wilderness areas of United States and Canada and along many a trout stream in wild and less wild places, I have had unusual opportunities for observation. Although I have never been able to keep a regular journal, I have slavishly kept detailed journals of all of these trips. I have also kept, off and on over the years, journals of nature sites closer to home as well.

As with Peter Parnall, the creator of this book, an interest in owls has been of the ever-since-I-can-remember variety. Peter speaks for himself in this joint introduction. His intense and affectionate interest in owls is consummated by his drawings, and they speak for him more eloquently than I can.

Peter Parnall and I first talked of an owl book in 1960 when as an editor, I first saw his rich folio of oils and drawings of his favorite bird. It has been a very great pleasure for me to put this short personal text alongside his drawings. Although I am a collaborator on this book and thus should not venture to praise any part of it, I am casting aside this small propriety by saying that in my opinion Peter's drawings are a notable contribution to the art of the owl.

9

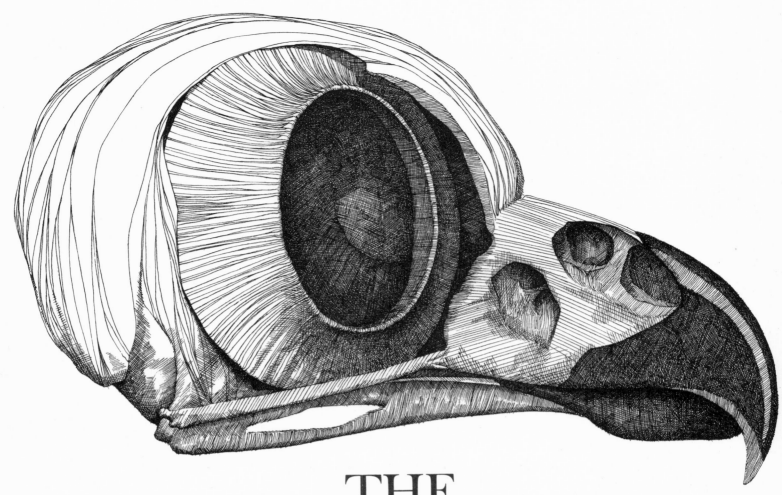

THE MORPHOLOGY OF OWLS

O wls are folk representatives from the world of birds and are virtually unique in their special age-old relationship to man. But they are also unique because of their physiology, in ways that are extremely interesting to scientists in general, and to ornithologists, physiologists, and morphologists in particular. And many of these special characteristics of owls can be as fascinating to the layman as to the biologist. Robert Payne's marvelous research in the hearing of barn owls is surely as engaging and full of wonders to laymen as it was to his fellow scientists,

and the same can be said for Brayton's astounding discoveries about the night-flying proclivities of bats. And the Craighead brothers' studies of owl populations and their prey is a masterpiece of bird demography.

In addition to their specialized beaks, feet, and talons, which equip them for predation, owls have other unique structures that sepparate them from most other birds. Here we will take note of four of the most interesting: their eyesight, hearing, flight and feathers, and, oddly enough, their digestion.

Perhaps because the owl is so seldom observed by the average person, there is much misinformation about the bird. No "fact" is more widespread, nor more false, than that owls "cannot see in the daytime." "Blind as a bat" is a phrase that leaps to the minds of most people when they think of the owl, for knowing that this bird has excellent night sight, and perhaps having observed in daylight their myopic appearance, the word has gotten around that this bird is handicapped by strong light. Actually, owls have the most versatile eyesight of all birds, and while it is true that they have remarkable ability to pick up light in very low exposures, they are also equipped to see quite well during the day. All birds have eyes enormously enlarged in comparison to their weight and size, and owls are especially distinguished by this characteristic. The larger owls, which weigh less than a fiftieth of the weight of the average man, have eyes that are as big as those of an adult human. The eyeballs of birds, however, are quite a different shape from those of man, so that the small skull of the creature may accomodate the large eyes. The owl has what is called a tubular eye, and this elongated specialization permits the lens-cornea section to be quite large in relation to the rest of the eye in order to gather and concentrate all possible light. For this reason the back part of the owl's eye has evolved so that it is much reduced in area, and the lens is set far back in the tube so that, as any camera buff will understand, a wide retina is not required in order to cover a wide field of view. But this huge eye within the relatively small skull of the bird is thus even less maneuverable than that of other birds. This extreme immobility of the owl's eye is compensated for, however, by a remarkably well-developed set of neck muscles. When an object moves out of the owl's lateral range he merely turns his head (which he can do with amazing speed) instead of rolling his eyeball towards that object. The owl can actually turn his head 270 of the full 360 degrees of a circle. Anyone who has walked around an owl in the daytime and watched him follow the circling threat has been amazed at the speed with which the bird can swivel his head on that well-muscled neck and pick up the observer on the opposite side. So fast is this motion, that many an observer has sworn the owl can turn his head completely around. No wonder he gives the impression of wringing his own neck!

But the eye of the owl has a further specialization that makes his eyesight so versatile. Unlike that of most birds, whose eyesight is monocular, the owl, with both eyes in the front of his head, can focus them together on one object, and thus has binocular sight the same as man. This characteristic improves the ability to judge distance accurately and thus "advantages" the bird in pursuing and seizing moving prey.

But owl eyes have yet another characteristic that gives still another level to the versatility of their eyesight. The minute visual cells in the retina of all eyes, the receptors that form the images of eyesight, are of two shapes and functions. The cones, named for their cone-like shape, function in bright light and enable the seer to distinguish color and to receive sharp visual images. The rods, also named for their shape, are the receptors that

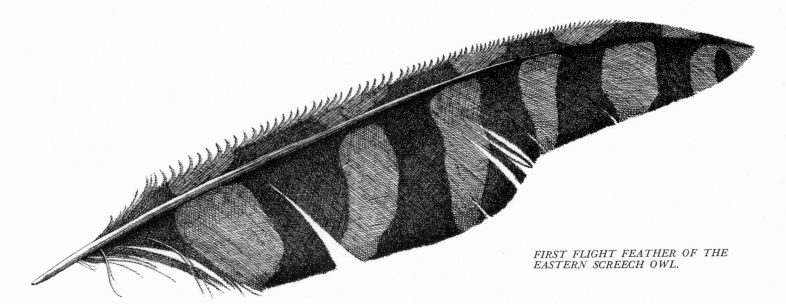

function in low light intensities and provide "night sight." Owls have a rich mixture of rods in their retina and thus have excellent night sight. On the other hand, owls also have enough of the cone receptor cells to be able to see better in daylight than at night. In his book *The Verterbrate Eye*, Gordon L. Walls reports a series of daytime experiments with a great horned owl that showed the bird could distinguish extremely high flying hawks that the human eye could not pick up at all.

But no creature, not even owls, no matter how well equipped with rods in the retina for night sight, can actually see in the dark. Yet it is well known that owls do catch their prey in conditions of near-total darkness. The solution to this mystery has been given by Robert Payne through his experiments with barn owls. Mr. Payne proved that not only can owls capture their prey in near-darkness, they can actually do it under conditions of *total* darkness.

The clue to this discovery was perhaps first given by a British ornithologist just before the turn of the century. Noting that the ears of owls are asymmetrical (the right and left ears and ear openings are not only differently shaped and of unequal size, but usually one ear opening is above and the other below the horizontal) this scientist suggested that the asymmetry of the owl's ears might help the bird in locating its prey. Robert Payne, through a long series of controlled experiments, proved that barn owls could capture mice under conditions of total darkness. Furthermore, the bird's "radar" was such that the owl could make its swoop toward the mouse with only about one degree of error on the vertical and horizontal! Mr. Payne's summary of his experiment gives fascinating insight into this remarkable characteristic of the owl's hearing devices.

For Mr. Payne's full summary all owl buffs should read his article in *The Living Bird, First Annual of the Cornell Laboratory of Ornithology, 1962*, entitled "How the Barn Owl Locates Prey by Hearing."

But night sight and aural asymmetry do not exhaust the owl's specialized abilities as a unique bird of prey. Owls also have a curious feather structure that permits them, when they wish, to fly with moth-like silence. In his engaging and informative book, *Flashing*

Wings, John A. Terres, former editor of *Audubon* magazine, comments on this further equipment of the owl. He says:

Some of the big, soft-feathered owls have remarkable and noisy courtship flights—surprising in these usually silent-flying birds of the night. Ordinarily, owls hunt without making wing noises. As they flap or glide silently through woodlands or over fields, they are quick to swerve or dive down upon an unwary mouse, rabbit, or other animal of the night. Their wings are broad and long, with slotted primaries (a high-lift wing) like the wings of the high soaring eagles and hawks that hunt by day. But the wings of an owl have a marvelous adaptation that enables them to fly without a sound.

The leading edges of their wings are finely toothed—like the tiny jagged teeth of a small saw. August Raspet, a scientist who specializes in studies in the biophysics of bird flight, believed that these toothed edges on the first flight feather silences any noise of the vortex of air rushing over the flying owl's wings.

The eyesight, hearing, and flight of owls combine to make this bird a deadly raptor by night as well as by day.

Owls require an enormous amount of food, as all birds do. They have an extremely high metabolism, and can process each day the equivalent of their own total body weight in food (see chapter on barn owls). Furthermore, birds of prey do not masticate their food, but bolt small creatures such as mice and lemmings, or hunks of meat from larger prey such as rabbits, skunks, and large birds, in one or two eye-blinking and neck-stretching gulps. The owls thus ingest fur, feathers,

beak, toes, nails, claws, and bones, and though their digestion is swift, it is not able to process such an assortment of trash and waste.

But through evolution this problem has been solved for owls just as it has for hawks and other predaceous birds. The gizzards of owls reject the horrendous miscellany and the bird regurgitates this waste material in neat pellets which cover the ground beneath nests and feeding perches. These pellets contain all the waste material in a felt-like elongated ball of fur, feather, and bone. This characteristic has enabled the ornithologist to learn much about the feeding habits of owls. Specialists can identify even small fragments of bone as that *Peromyscus* or some other species of mouse. Furthermore, such experts can make a close estimate of the proportion of various prey species in the total intake of of the meat-eating birds. It is, indeed, such studies that have shown that the owl, in addition to being a fascinating bird for its lore, its mystery, and its strange physiology, is also one of the most useful to man of all the wild creatures in controlling pests and in maintaining the balance of nature.

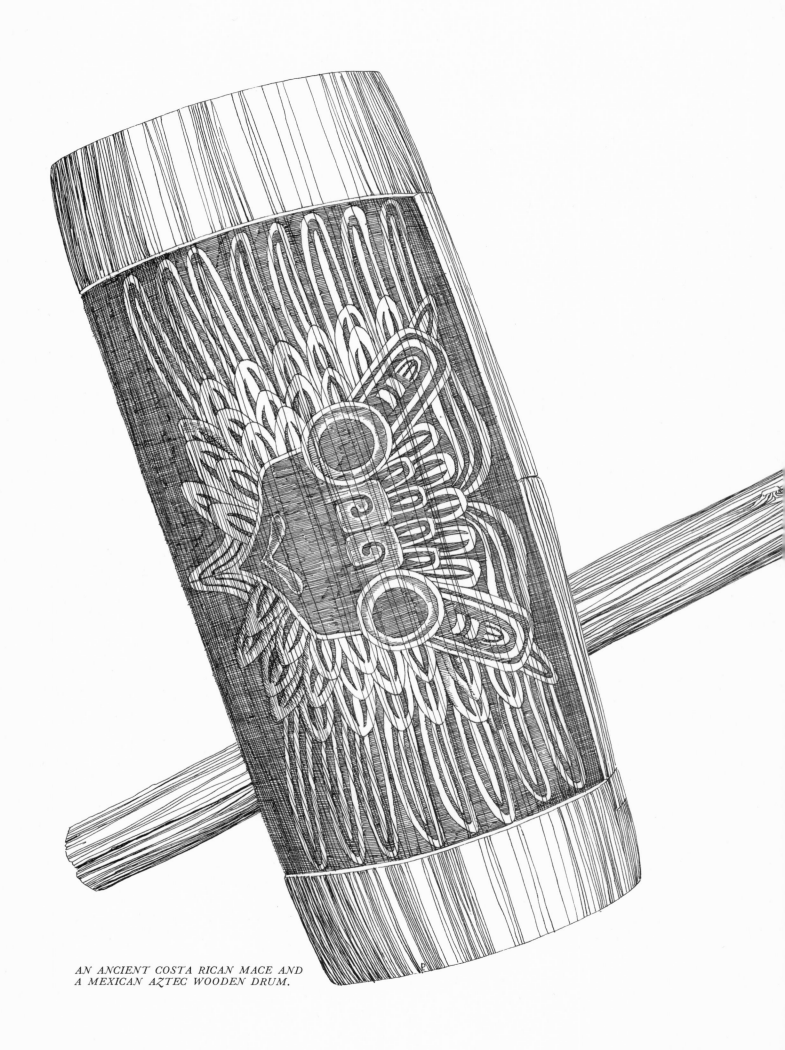

AN ANCIENT COSTA RICAN MACE AND
A MEXICAN AZTEC WOODEN DRUM.

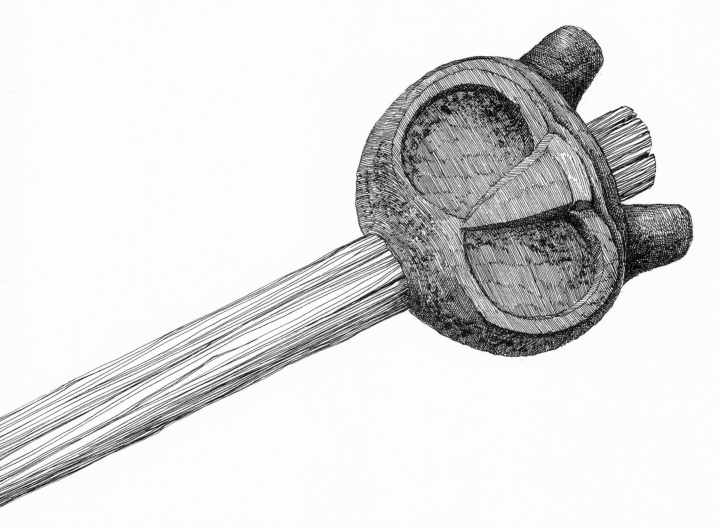

FOLKLORE OF OWLS

Peter Parnall stands at the end of an ancient artistic tradition, for the first drawing ever made by man of a bird that can be identified by species was that of an owl. In a way this is fitting, for since the day that Old Stone Age engraving so easily indentifiable as a representation of the snowy owl was scratched on the wall of the cave called *Les Trois Frères*, men have been continuously preoccupied by owls. Owls have served as totem animals; they have been the companions of gods and goddesses in the pantheons of deities; they have figured and still figure prominently in human folklore and literature. Today the owl's continued appeal is evidenced by the thousands of collectors of owl statues and figurines. Indeed as recently as two years ago the universal appeal of owls was demonstrated by the fact that a prominent New York City department store devoted a full page advertisement at Christmas time to the numerous porcelain, glass, and wooden owl figures that could be had at the store's sales counters.

Undoubtedly the fascination owls have had for men predates the Cro-Magnon who made

15

the cave painting; the eerie hoots and near-human screams and gobblings of owls, which even in our relatively unsuperstitious times can produce a tiny shiver of fear on a dark night, more powerfully affected men in past millennia more ancient than the times of the cave painters.

A bird that flies by night, when the mysteries and terrors of life have always been most rampant in men's minds, was certain to have an awesome place in men's imaginations. In times when every inanimate object and living creature was thought to be possessed by spirits, the owl must have seemed dire and fearsome indeed. His very appearance is unlike that of other birds; his eyes set in the front of his face where they can stare in man-like fashion at his observer add a strong touch of the human to his aspect. His weird hoots, screams, demoniac laughter, and gobblings and chucklings lend a devilish character that draws him compulsively into the human (or superhuman) world. His solemn mien, his level, two-eyed glare, his dignity of stance and upright perch give him a quality of reserve that seems to spell wisdom and self-contained insight. The phrase, "wise old owl," must reflect a judgment about the bird that is very old in man's lore. The Greeks associated the owl with their patroness, Athena, the goddess of knowledge and wisdom. The big-eyed judgment of the wise bird looked out from the obverse side of Athenian coins at generations of Greeks who thought of the Little Owl (*Athena noctua*) as a symbol of their own superior

qualities. Although the overt association of the owl with wisdom comes to us most directly from the Greeks, long before their time the owl figured in human folklore as a bird of power and portent. In fact, Athena herself seems to have been a goddess derived from an Anatolian female deity, an earth goddess of fertility. The owl may have been associated with this earlier figure or its association with Athena may have come more mundanely from the fact that it nested amongst the buildings of the Acropolis. It is natural that the owl should be associated with darkness, and therefore with the underworld. Indeed, Lilith herself, Sumerian goddess of the underworld, whose name is translated in the Authorized Version of the Bible as "screech owl," is represented on an ancient cult plaque as winged, taloned, and flanked by two owls. The goddess holds in her hands measuring ropes, symbols of judgment. It is interesting in this connection that the famous "owl cups" so common in Greek ceramics may also have been used as measures, and thus as standards or as symbols of judgment. Owls appear as mummies among the grave furniture in Egypt and commonly on tomb paintings. In China, the owl was the symbol of thunder and lightning, and was portrayed in ornaments called "owl corners" which were built into the corners of roofs to protect the dwelling from fire.

The owl's configuration in folklore is early, worldwide and universal, and for this reason folklorists have been intrigued by man's preoccupation with the bird. Anyone who wishes to pursue the subject should read the book, *Folklore of Birds* by the British ornithologist,

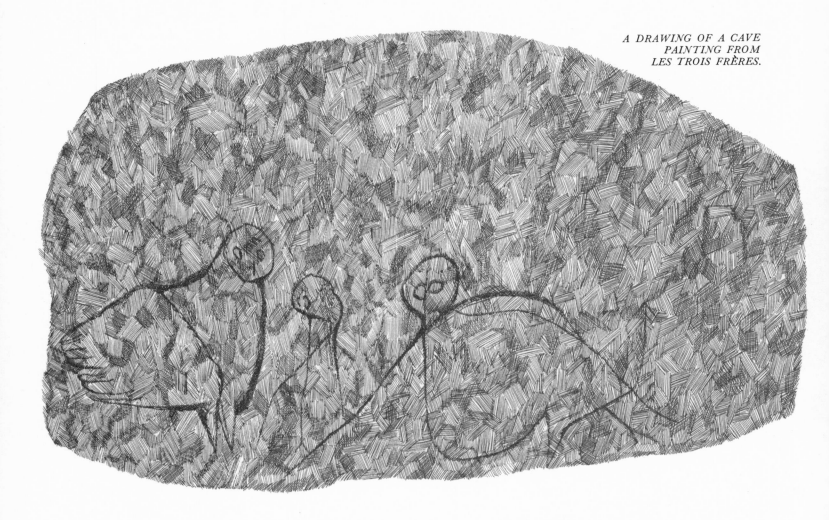

E. A. Armstrong. His chapter "Night's Black Agents" (Chapter 7) is devoted to owls.

In many parts of Europe and Asia, merely seeing an owl called for countersigns and propitiatory rites. The owl, however, was not only an early portent of evil and even a common harbinger of death but like all associates of shamans, sorcerers, and necromancers, became a symbol that in the proper hands could avert or turn aside evil. This conversion of a symbol of evil into a thing endowed with beneficent powers is common in man's history and the process is well described by E. A. Armstrong: "So the owl which terrifies folk by gazing at them with its two great eyes or by wailing or shrieking like a soul in torment may be enlisted against the many powers of evil with which it is associated. The visible object of fear may be employed to inspire fear in the invisible powers which are feared. Thus the evil thing can be transformed into an ally by enlisting it against evil. But for the exploitation of this principle in the vaccines of modern medicine many of us would not be alive today."

The cave painter of *Les Trois Frères* was probably a shaman himself working his magic in the depths of darkness in the grottoes, rendering his creatures for magical purposes. It seems most likely that the snowy owls may have thus had the apotropaic function described so well by Mr. Armstrong.

From the British Isles to China the owl has been associated with evil deeds. When Shakespeare has Macbeth cry, "I have done the deed; didst thou hear a noise?" and his lady replies,

It was the owl that shriek'd, the fatal bellman
Which gives the stern'st good-night . . .
I heard the owl scream and the crickets cry

she was making an association most ancient in human lore.

And the witches had anticipated her, for when the cauldron boiled they added an owlet's wing to that infernal brew. The witches and Lady Macbeth were making an association most ancient in human lore. Both Jeremiah and Isaiah in leveling curses predicted that "owls shall dwell therein," and many cultures have formulae in their magic for pacifying the forces of evil when an owl alights on a dwelling place. Although Pliny himself was skeptical about the matter, he reports the superstition that death follows the owl that perches atop a private house and national disaster occurs when the same bird roosts in a public building. When Casca says, in *Julius Caesar*:

And yesterday the bird of night did sit
Even at noonday, upon the market place
Hooting and shrieking.

he is following Plutarch who in turn must have followed Pliny's sources, which were not from literature but from lore.

Thus "the bird that snatches the soul,"

REPRESENTATION OF AN EGYPTIAN RELIEF CARVING

as the Chinese put it, was almost universally an omen of death and doom. And lest we get the notion that these superstitions are a thing of the distant past, it may be useful to quote further Mr. Armstrong: "W. J. Brown, writing in 1934, mentions that when he commented to an old man on the death of a mutual acquaintance, he remarked, 'It weren't no more than I expected. I come past his house one night, and there were a scret (screech) owl on his roof, scretting something horrible. I always reckon to take note of them things.' "

Whether or not the old man had an antidote for the evil of owls, other men have had. Just as the hex sign painted on the side of a barn is meant to avert evil, so the owl or

19

A GREEK COIN FROM ATHENS, ABOUT 500 B.C.

owl wings, nailed on the side or door of a barn, is evidence of a continuation of the ancient belief that the owl was "strong medicine" and could turn aside bad luck. Owl broth turns up regularly in folk pharmacopoeia as a remedy for children's diseases, and parts of the owl, such as its foot or heart, were thought to be cures for ailments as diverse as madness, bad eyesight, and heart disease. The Romans used an owlish design to counteract the evil eye, and the Altaic people in far off Central Asia kept the bird itself near a child's bed to fend off evil spirits. In Japan, the Ainu nailed representations of owls to their houses in times of epidemics or famine. Alcoholism, epilepsy, and gout have variously been treated by the eggs and flesh of owls.

To some, the owl's powers could far transcend their use in private ministrations. In *The Wasps*, written in 422 B.C., Aristophanes attributed the victory at Marathon to the fact that "Pallas sent her night bird." And Agathocles, Tyrant of Syracuse, claimed that his stunning victory over the Carthaginians in 310 B.C. was due to his release of owls over his army.

The appearance of owls in the folklore and art of pre-Columbian America may have stemmed from ancient lore carried across the Bering Straits by the forebears of the American Indian and Eskimo, or it may have arisen afresh here because people made the same association between owls and the supernatural that the Europeans and Asiatics made. The owl turns up as a canny creature in Eskimo lore and as a worthy antagonist to the sly coyote in the lore of the Zunis and other southwestern American Indians. The Mixtecs and Zapotecs have fine owl tales to tell, often memorialized on their ceramics. The Mayans associated the owl with child bearing and indicated this by the use of the bird as part of a headdress on female figurines. The night bird's association with the moon, and that body's association the world over with fertility, has been noted previously.

The Mayans put the owl in a classic position that harks back to Lilith herself, for the screech owl was the symbol of Ah Puch, the god of death who ruled the lowest level in the underworld. It was left to the Aztecs, however, to make the ultimate association of the owl with death. As Faith Medlin reports in her interesting book, *Centuries of Owls*, "During the rites of human sacrifice, stone containers such as the *cuauhxicalli* with the owl motif were used by priests to hold the hearts that were torn from the prisoners and offered to the gods. *Teponaztli* (drums), carved from hollowed-out logs and adorned with an owl face, beat dramatic tempos during the gory ceremonies. The Aztecs associated the owl with the god of the dead. Even today many descendants of those Aztec warriors believe the owl's night cry is fatal to anyone who hears its portentous call." And many descendants of other warriors from other cultures still half believe it today.

Thus, the owl figurine that sits on your occasional table or what-not shelf is an ancient and universal symbol of power and portent. As fascinating as is the relationship between this bird and man, the bird alone is even more engaging. He is unique, as we shall see, in more ways than in his folklore.

THE SCREECH OWL

My Aunt Roxie, my father's younger sister, is a vigorous and spirited person, and some of my fondest memories of my grandfather's Indiana farm are connected with the products of her lively imagination. I remember many a cozy night sitting in my grandfather's parlor playing Parchesi under the pleasant, soft yellow light of the natural gas lamp that hung from the ceiling. As often as not, when the game ended, a period of terrifying ghost-story telling would ensue. Or my aunt would regale us with stirring tales of her adventures in Mexico during the outbreak of the 1912 Revolution. These tales were bizarre and scary, far removed from familiar farm scenes. As the lamps hissed

their sleepy sibilant sounds, we kids would be magically transported to strange places where eerie happenings were commonplace. My aunt's hushed voice would titillate us with gloomy scenes in haunted houses, graveyards, and other ghoulish places.

Often some night sound would intrude—the scurrying of a mouse in the attic, or the rustling of some nameless bird or animal whose noise would startle us.

"Whassat?" my aunt would hiss, and eyes would grow rounder and breaths would be held until the alarm in my aunt's voice could be dissipated by the normal, gratefully familiar meow of a cat, or by some other noise which could be explained rationally.

My aunt's very best ally in these chilling little episodes was, of course, the screech owl, whose wavering, tremulous cry was the "skeeriest" of all. The soft silence of a summer night is never so fearfully shattered as when this little owl gives voice to his lonely, shivery little call. He often supplied a long, chilling chorus to Aunt Roxie's fearsome tales.

The screech owl is sometimes seen in the daylight, roosting close to some tree trunk.

He is a blinker, sometimes showing one eye open, the other a slanted slit; then he opens the slit to blink lugubriously at the intruder. I used to watch a screech owl that had evidently nested in a big knothole in a cedar tree in the corner of my grandfather's front yard. He stayed in this hole and amazed my cousin and me by appearing one night as a cinnamon red little bird, then amazingly the next night, as gray as a weathered old board.

We conjectured about how this little owl could seemingly change his color at will until one night we saw them both at once, one red, one gray. The screech owl (like the ruffled grouse) is dimorphic and comes in two color phases.

Years after my first experience with the screech owl, I observed another in the very same cedar tree one early summer night. Sitting in the porch swing (a massive leather upholstered seat from an old Reo hung by chains from the porch ceiling), I was drowsily digesting a farmer's heavy supper. My attention was caught by a bird flying out and back from a branch in the old cedar. I slipped into the house and got a flashlight with which I soon "shined" a screech owl. He had something in his beak which he swallowed with a couple of slow, neck-stretching gulps. He was not disturbed by the sudden light so I sat down in the grass with my back against the rough trunk of a big willow to watch.

In the next half hour or so, the owl made four or five quick forays from his perch. In the moonlight, his sortie could be seen in silhouette against the lighter sky. He would leave the branch suddenly in jerky, tilting flight of sudden turns and twists, and then return to his perch. His sudden flight and return reminded me of the kingbird's. He was surely feeding on some night flying creature. Arising and moving swiftly toward the cedar I "shined" him again. This time I was sure that what he held in his beak was a "June bug." And this time he *was* disturbed and flew across the fence into the apple orchard. I returned to the comfort of the swing. The inside light shone through the screen door onto the porch floor before me. There, struggling clumsily to right itself, its feet futilely pawing the air, was a June bug that had doubtless struck the screen and fallen. I remember wondering if the little screech owl ever "worked" the front porch when no one was around to disturb his hunt. June bugs always remind me of screech owls.

When one examines the considerable literature on this little owl it becomes clear at once why Arthur Bent referred to this one as he did when he said, "If the great horned owl can rightly be called a 'feathered tiger,' the screech owl deserves to be called a 'feathered wildcat,' for it certainly is a savage little brute . . ." The screech owl is smaller than a robin, but his small size belies his prowess as a hunter. Although all owls take a wide variety of creatures for food, the screech owl seems equipped to prey on almost anything that his size does not preclude. He is not a rodent specialist like the barn owl, but mice, shrews, and even rats form a major part of the screech owl's diet. He is also a bird hunter, insect catcher, and, like the great horned owl, a very successful fisherman. His hunting techniques have to be most versatile, for when he is not sallying forth from a tree limb catching, in fly-catcher style, the night-flying insects, or coursing on his large silent wings over fields, woods, and out-buildings after mice, he may actually patrol afoot stretches of woods and pavement where mice may cross from their nests to grain field feeding areas. Or he will wade the shallows of streams and ponds after crayfish and bullheads. In the dryer parts of his range he is a lizard hunter, and his pellets

show that he is also a regular harvester of night-dormant grasshoppers, plucking these nice morsels from grass stems in the fields like a fruit picker.

He may be thought of as a regular busy-body of a hunter, for his prey includes an astonishing variety of species of all sizes, habits, and degree of formidability. Further, he is a little wildcat of a night hunter. The pesky house sparrow is an easy prey, as are other small birds. But he is on record as a hunter of much bigger birds, too. Pigeons seem to present no problem to him; he has even been known to take grouse; and in at least one instance—though this, to be sure, must be a most rare occurrence—the little wildcat was observed trying to make off with a full sized hen. He is a very strong-footed owl for his size.

When seen perching, the screech owl presents two quite different silhouettes. On occasion he seems a solid, blocky bird, almost square in outline. But at other times the same owl will appear much more elongated, slim, tall and narrow. Once, while observing a screech owl perched in a tree on the steep side of a deep, wet ravine, I saw the transformation take place. When first glimpsed, the little bird squatted compactly, but upon seeing my motion it straightened into a height that seemed twice its first dimension. Even its ear tufts were held more erect, adding to its greater height. One would have thought him a different bird. This owl was in the gray phase and his mottled feathers looked very much like the rough graying bark of an old tree.

Those who have seen the nests report five eggs an average brooding clutch. The nests usually are found in the natural cavity of some old tree or in a woodpecker's former abode. The eggs are laid on the old chips and rubbish found in such holes; the owl seems happy with whatever furnishings are already at hand. In twenty-one to thirty days, with the average about twenty-six, the eggs hatch. The owlets, large-headed and covered at first with a white fleecy down, are awkward and bumbling when very young, but within a few days the blooming pin feathers begin to show and the down takes on a dirty gray color. Their voracious demands keep the parents busy providing food. One observer during a period of seven successive days in late June and early July recorded that these feedings began between 8:25 and 9:12 P.M.; the earliest quitting time was 1:40 A.M., the latest 4:15 A.M. During those seven nights the parent birds made a variable number of feeding trips: 20, 73, 36, 14, 75, 67, and 72. The fifth night's observation (from 8:34 P.M. to 1:40 A.M.) produced two beetles and *seventy-three* moths. The morning after this same night the observer's wife noted, however, the new feathers of six birds in the nest —phoebe, scarlet tanager, cedar waxwing, chipping sparrow, redstart, and catbird— evidently the screech owl does his bird hunting nearer dawn when the prey birds are beginning to stir on their perches.

The slit-eyed squint of the little screech owl, the smallest of the "eared" owls, will be the easiest way to identify him when you surprise him on his perch, but most people will note his presence by hearing his spooky wavering tremolo.

THE PYGMY OWL

January 28, 1950 was an especially good day for me. Not only was I in the company of the late J. Frank Dobie, but on that day I saw no fewer than seven species of birds for the first time in my experience. The most notable of these was the pygmy owl. Mr. Dobie was congratulating himself for having shown me a canyon wren when, ahead of us in the dry bed of a stream high above the Devil's River, we spotted a tiny owl perched on the tip of a cactus. The canyon wren was forgotten, for here was a fine specimen of the ferruginous pygmy owl. With his tail cocked sassily, the little owl let us approach quite close before flapping up over the low canyon wall. One year later, while camped high in the San Juans in Colorado, I saw the Rocky Mountain variety of this tiny owl on several occasions, for one regularly hunted the grassy meadow surrounding a beaver pond close to where our tents were pitched. Not only because he was diurnal, but for other reasons the Rocky Mountain pygmy owl reminds one

28

of the hawk owl. The little Colorado owl liked to perch high in a dead stub, just as the hawk owl is wont to do. And when he swooped from one perch to another he flew with rapid wing beats in a deep sweep downward, coming quite close to the grasstops, then rising in a shorter but graceful curve just before taking his next perch. Bent describes the little owl as "scarcely as big as a bluebird, and not nearly so large as a robin." He is a generalized feeder, hunting birds, mammals, lizards, snakes, and a variety of insects as his prey. A savage little gamecock of a bird, he'll take on anything up to the size of pocket gophers as long as they are "not more than twice the owl's own size." Perhaps the most widely distributed of all the small earless owls in the West, this little bird regularly summers in the mountains at altitudes between 5,000 and 10,000 feet. He loves the woodlands, especially pine. My little San Juan pygmy was doing his hunting at 9,000 feet and the time was late October. Although I did not see this owl make a catch that I could identify, on several occasions after I had come in from a day's hunting I did see him swoop down into the border of the pond, seemingly after a mouse. There is something neat looking about the pygmy. Perhaps it is his relatively small head compared to the heads of other small owls. The saw whet and the boreal, for example, both small owls, though larger than the pygmy, have big heads in comparison to their bodies. The pygmy owl also has a slightly longer tail in relation to his size than other owls. In this, too, the pygmy owl reminds the observer of the hawk owl. But it is his little rounded

head that gives him an extra daintiness.

The pygmy owl is rusty or gray-brown in color, with rather widely-spaced black stripes down his light breast. In the adult, the top of his head and shoulders are spotted with small, light spots. One of the most distinguishing characteristics, however, is the black, somewhat elongated patch that begins just behind the facial disk and extends down and back on the neck. Size, flight, small-headedness, distinct stripes on the breast, the black neck patch, and the long tail cocked when perching mark this fine owl. The Rocky Mountain pygmy ranges from Canada south through the mountains to southern California, New Mexico and Arizona; the ferruginous ranges from the lower Rio Grande up into southern Arizona.

This owl tries to find a nice vacant woodpecker's nest—any size up to that of the flicker will do—about eight to ten feet above the ground. The hen lays three or four white eggs, the same size as those of the robin, in the woody bottom of the nest. The eggs tend to be rounder than those of most birds. Nesting usually takes place from the tenth of May to the end of June and one authority (Bent) says the incubation of the eggs starts as soon as the first egg is layed.

Jays, wrens, blackbirds, orioles, even hummingbirds regularly harrass the pygmy owl, a confirmation perhaps of the catholicity of this owl's food tastes. In this the pygmy is like the screech and great horned owls: they'll eat most anything they are big enough to tackle and they will tackle anything up to and even exceeding, occasionally, their own weight and size.

RICHARDSON'S OWL

Richardson's owl, sometimes called the boreal owl, is a charming bird. He is named for Sir John Richardson (1767–1865), the Scot who as traveler and naturalist has had his name memorialized in several creatures, including the Richardson barren ground grizzly.

Since he is a true northerner and is only very occasionally seen south of our Canadian border, one is lucky indeed to have this owl on one's life list. And besides, he is determinedly nocturnal, and rarely seen in the daytime even in his range. My boreal owls are two, both seen near the Alatna River in

northern Alaska and both seen perched on the limb of a black spruce in broad daylight. One of these I collected for an ornithologist's study skin and could thus examine him carefully. The other was almost equally available, for he allowed me to come close enough to have picked him up had I been able to reach him. He was not alarmed in any way and seemed in his foolish tameness to bear out the name the Eskimos have given him, tukwelinguk, "the blind one."

This owl is scarcely bigger than a saw whet owl (which it resembles to some degree) and has the contours of a slightly conventionalized

figurine. He is a kind of toy owl, and the more charming for it. Superficially he reminds one of the screech owl, for he is about the same size (nine to eleven inches), but unlike the screech owl he is earless. He is also big-headed, and curiously so, for his head is flat topped, even slightly concave, and framed in brown in its top outline. His facial disks are distinctly pale gray, and into the V formed from their arches his forehead is spotted with small white dots. His upper parts are a rich brown, again spotted quite distinctly with white, and his breast and belly are white with distinct brown stripes. His tail is barred with half a dozen stripes in white. His large wings enable him to flap slowly through the dark Arctic night and with unusual maneuverability.

This self-possessed little owl lives in the heavy northern evergreen woods where like so many of his relatives he hunts voles, mice, and lemmings, and perhaps birds and insects. Not much is actually known of his habits. He nests in hollow trees, often using the abandoned nests of pileated woodpeckers, although at times he will use the stick nests of other birds. The hen lays four to six white eggs.

I think of this owl as the chickadee among owls. He encourages this notion because, like the chickadee, his very diminutiveness gives him a valiant quality as a year round resident of the coldest climes. He seems too small, somehow, to face the icy blasts of the Arctic. At least the chickadee has company in his airy flock neighbors. The boreal owl, a loner like most owls, sits in solitude in the sub-zero darkness of the sunless Arctic winter and makes a good living there on that little haymaker, the vole, and other rodents.

One great naturalist, Charles H. Merriam, has left a succinct description of the call of this bird: "A low note that resembles the sound produced by water dropping from a height." His call must be as appealing as his size for Arthur Bent likens it to a "soft, high-pitched bell," and Ernest Thompson Seton, who was also fortunate enough to hear the boreal's call, confirms Bent by rendering the sound as "ting, ting, ting."

THE SNOWY OWL

"No, he not fly fast like that hawk but okpik fly a long time." This was how the Eskimo Kisik, with whom we were camped at the mouth of the Colville River in northern Alaska, answered my question about the snowy owl. The lonely, mysterious tundra lay about us. Flat prairie stretched as far as our eyes could see, broken only by our own shadows and by the dwarf willow-fringed channels of the Colville's delta. We had just seen a gyrfalcon swoop into a cackling covey of ptarmigan—a flash of wings, the flight of the arrow-like body, the end-over-end tumble of the stricken ptarmigan. The falcon executed a tight turn, made a one-foot pick up of his quarry from just above the muddy flat of the dry channel, and was gone beyond the willows. My query came from my curiosity about whether the owl, too, preyed on the ptarmigan.

"Okpik eat him, too," Kisik had said with an appreciative grin. Kisik, like most Eskimos, was a fine observer and an enthusiastic one. But he was also thoughtful about this knowledge, always doing his best to instruct me with careful answers from his great fund of functional information on the Arctic's animals and birds.

I thought for a moment about the owl's heavy, methodical flight. "Can okpik fly as fast as the hawk flies, fast enough to catch the ptarmigan?"

Kisik's answer about the owl's lack of speed compared to the gyrfalcon's had brought my inevitable next question.

"Then how does he catch the ptarmigan?"

"Oh, he not catch him at first—owl scare up many ptarmigan but he follow one. That ptarmigan fly a little then he come down. Okpik keep right on. Ptarmigan fly again and okpik he not get tired, he keep right on. Pretty soon ptarmigan get tired. Okpik say to himself, 'Pretty soon I catch that ptarmigan.' Ptarmigan fly into willows then he hide there, maybe. Pretty tired now. But okpik go right into willows too. He hop around there some but he catch his supper all right."

I had relished my friend's phrase "hop around some" for it described most graphically what I myself had observed. Our camp that summer and fall was pitched at Niglik Point on the last high-cut bank of the Colville River just before its channel widened into a series of mud flats and emptied its muddy water into the Arctic Ocean. Niglik was an ancient fishing camp on the westernmost channel of the Colville's thirty-mile-wide delta. It had a fine ice house dug down seven feet into the perma frost of the loess. Its opening was covered by a miniature sod ïgloo and access to its charnel depths was had by a driftwood ladder. In the olden times, said Kisik, Niglik was the site of the annual trade meeting between the coastal peoples and those who made their livings inland in the Brooks Range. A hundred yards beyond Kisik's abandoned sod and driftwood winter igloo, the tundra was pimpled by *pingaluks*, those characteristic frost-heaves of the tundra. These two-foot-high mounds, the size of a living-room rug, provide the "high" relief on the otherwise table-flat tundra. The snowy owls nest on them and later use them as hunting perches. Sometimes one finds the den of the Arctic ground squirrel burrowed into the same *pingaluk* that holds the nest of the owl and one wonders whether the inhabitant had been eaten before the owls built their nest.

I had mounted a thirty-power spotting scope on top of an empty oil drum and used it to watch caribou, and on one occasion seals, swans, geese, loons, and ducks, but above all snowy owls. These fine birds fascinated me above all other creatures. A num-

ber of late nesters could be seen at various ranges and at various times. I investigated these at closer range, always intrigued by the unfamiliar pose of a brooding owl. Somehow, such a characteristically upright bird always looks strange while nesting. A snowy owl always seems to be at his perch throughout the twenty-four hours of light of the short Arctic summer. One owl I spotted with the scope was almost totally white, probably a male. One could see only a few flecks of gray feathers on his breast and back. With the scope trained on him he seemed as close at hand as a museum study skin. Between me and his lemon yellow eyes was the lovely varigation of color of the low flowering grasses that brightened the tundra's spongy sod.

Kisik, speaking of the snowy owl's hunting habits, once said, "That okpik is lazy hunter sometimes. He chase ptarmigan but he wait for mouse." And wait this okpik did. For long periods this white sentinel waited. His dreamy, rather innocent stare, unblinking and ingenuous, took in his surroundings with seeming disinterest. He has always struck me as the perfunctory dreamer among owls. His expression—if a bird can be said to have an expression; I think this *can* be said of owls —is that of an owlish Colonel Blimp. The heavily feathered lores nearly conceal the black beak and give the appearance of a bluff white mustache. The eyes are set nearer the top of the round, almost earless head, than the eyes in most owls, and they are more narrow in the vertical dimension. The face, eyes and mustache combine to give him the rather sappy, fatuous stare of the retired, pre-war British colonel. Okpik just doesn't look quite bright. But he is alert enough, and as one of the two largest owls, he has great power as well.

"My" owl sat on his *pingaluk* and for the most part he sat motionless. Occasionally he would turn his head slowly, as if it were swivelled on ball bearings, and less often he would jerk his head swiftly in its turn as if alerted by some sudden, close-at-hand rustling in the low, soddy coverts about him. Like all birds, the owl must turn his head to see about him as his eyeballs do not maneuver in their sockets.

The snowy owl undoubtedly feeds on the Arctic ground squirrel quite regularly, and I share with the owl a liking for the flesh of these animals. But, judging from the pellets I found near the hummocky *pingaluks*, his diet during the summer months is mostly made up of mice and lemmings. "He catch sikrik, all right," Kisik told me. "No use to hunt sikrik where okpik stay." Each year Kisik and his wife, Oineok, make a late summer outing when they hunt and trap ground squirrels both for the pot and for the skins, which are used for lining winter clothing.

The owl I watched had a lazy hunter's technique with the mice. He simply waited for them to come to him. Seven times during my observations of this bird I saw him make kills, and on all occasions his tactics were basically the same. He would sit motionless on his low perch until a foraging mouse came close enough. Then he would jump forward, scarcely using his wings, and hop and scrabble clumsily about, leaping and grasping this way and that until he had seized (or sometimes lost) the panic-stricken mouse. Once or twice he flew off with his prey. Usually he returned to the *pingaluk*, the mouse clutched in one foot. There he would apparently mouth the mouse a few times, then straighten up with the mouse in his beak. A couple of gulps and the furry morsel was gone.

This owl would sometimes gape once or twice after he had swallowed the mouse, perhaps to clear his gullet.

The scramble on the ground appeared awkward and makeshift. Owls are clumsy walkers at best, and one would think from their walking gait that they would find ground pursuit unproductive. Actually they move fast, splaying out an armed foot here, hopping there, leaping on half-open wings, as the mouse's evasive action in the grasses requires. They may not have the blinding, sinuous speed of that finest of all mousers, the weasel, and their tactics may not have the grace seen in the pick-up of the short-eared owl, but they are nonetheless effective. Kisik said that the snowy owl caught ground squirrels in the same way, but that he had also seen the coursing owl capture this little rodent with a swift swoop from the wing.

The snowy owl's distribution over the tundra is hit and miss in design. Whole areas, as one observes them from a low-flying plane, may be devoid of owls, yet on one flight in 1952, fifty miles or so east from the mouth of the Colville, I observed an impressive concentration of these great white birds. The area appeared to the eye of an untrained observer to be five or six hundred square

yards. The tundra was pimpled with scores of frost heaves and about a third of these *pingaluks* were each decorated with an elongated pom-pom, a snowy owl. The green-gray tundra was literally white-dotted with these fine birds. The whole aspect was that of a low-keyed abstract expressionist painting, one derived from a limited pallet of fog and whitewash.

As one always does in such situations, I tried to count the whitish birds; by the time we had passed over the area I had got past an accurate count of twenty-three and was estimating another ten or a dozen beyond that number. Why such a concentration? Perhaps some special abundance of mice or lemmings. Whatever the reason, it was a memorable sight.

Eskimo ivory carvers, who can be both realistic or expressionistic in their art, capture beautifully in their works the round-faced, round-headed elongatedness of the snowy owl. And speaking of primitive artists, it is worthy of mention here that the very earliest representation of a bird by man is that of a family of snowy owls scratched by an Upper Paleolithic artist on a wall in a cave in the Dordogne region of France. Engraved 15,000 years ago in the Magdalenian period, these birds are unmistakably snowy owls, which then inhabited their favorite tundra country. That was southwestern France during the late stages of the Worm period of the Ice Age. These paintings have very similar flavor to that of an ivory carving I own, done by a West Coast Alaskan Eskimo. Both of these

tundra hunters saw the snowy owl in the same way.

Occasionally one sees this fine owl far south of this extreme northern range. When population crashes occur among northern rodents, the owl, like other predators, is forced to move to more favorable feeding grounds. These false migrations can sometimes be predicted when the low rodent cycle is anticipated by biologists.

Once, a number of years ago, my deer hunting partner, Joe MacLain, and I had climbed the summit of an Adirondack mountain to set up a camp near a pass between two basins. We topped the bald summit and crossed the narrow ridge to look down on the other side to a vast basin of hemlocks. There, a lone dwarf cedar clung bravely to the rocks just below the far lip of the ridge. From it, not a dozen feet away, a snowy owl flushed and flew lazily out into the wide, airy heights and sailed and flapped down in a wide-sweeping arc toward the thick cover far below. It was the first snowy owl I had ever seen south of the Arctic Circle. The view of this stranger, white against the dark green tops of the trees below me, was a subject to thrill an artist. It thrilled us.

Snowy owls appear in some numbers periodically in the northern United States and southern Canada and they have been sighted as far as southern California, Nevada, Oklahoma, Tennessee, and Georgia. Whether these hungry owls usually make their ways back home is something of which ornithologists are not sure. Probably most of them do.

The snowy owl and the great horned owl are our largest owls. Their wingspread is fifty to sixty inches, their length twenty-two to twenty-five inches and their bodies, say those who have weighed numbers of both species, are larger than those of the seemingly larger great gray owls. Contrary to the usual impression, the snowy owl is not entirely white. Sometimes the mottle on the breast and back is considerable; the color ranges from pure white to a gray-mottled phase, like the phases of the gyrfalcon. Some snowy owls appear as grayish rather than white. Ornithologists who have studied numbers of these owls say the males tend much more to pure or near-pure whiteness than females. Males may have a few smoky-black or slate-colored spots scattered over the upper parts with similar larger spots near the tips of primaries and tail feathers. The females are slightly larger than the males, and usually have a pure white face, sides of neck, chin and throat. Their feet and legs are also white. On both sexes the tarsus and toes are covered with long, hairy white feathers covering most of the black claws, which are long and handsomely curved.

Snowy owls usually nest on the ground and make a shallow saucer lightly lined with moss and feathers. I saw what appeared to be nesting owls on the lip of a high bluff of coal on the Colville River. The eggs, five to eight, are roughly surfaced and white or cream-white and the young owlets are first downy and white, then downy and brown. The young birds are much more strongly barred everywhere than adults of the same sex. Unlike those of precocial birds, the eggs hatch as they were laid, so that owlets of ascending sizes will be found in the same nest.

THE BARN OWL

The barn owl is surely the ghostly owl nonpareil. Many people who have seen this pale wraith on dark nights have associated him with haunts, spirits, and "skeery" things in general, and well they might, for the barn owl accommodates such emotions not only by his appearance but by his choice of habitat. His very name is a clue to his penchant for old buildings, unused silos, half-ruined barns and sheds, and abandoned houses, to say nothing of church steeples and windmills. In the days when my cousin Kenny and I were worm fishermen daring the dark of the moon and armed only with a coal oil lantern and two bamboo fishing poles, the very best "haunted house" we knew was one that stood vacant-eyed and forbidding above the best catfish hole along old Herrigan Creek. Once when we had grown just old enough to think we could scorn our former fears, we boldy approached the old house (in the waning *daylight*, however) to show ourselves that we were now above such kidstuff. We were scared out of our wits when we flushed one of these monkey-faced birds right out of his roosting place

in the eaves of the little house. I remember that he flew so close to my ears I could feel the brush of his wings as he swept through a glassless window and out into the trees behind the house.

I associate the barn owl with the last soft light of the fading summer day when the frantic wing beats of the skimming bat and the brainless thump and bump of the June bug on the screen door keep eerie company with the desultory calls of the katydid. Sometimes a late chore would take me to the barn lot after dark to close a hen house door or slop the hogs. I rarely would see this light bellied bird, who seemed bigger at night, fly in or out of the big hay-sling port in the barn. "Don't you boys bother the bird," my grandfather would warn, "he's a better ratter than old Trix will ever be." We—my cousin and I—were never sure whether we should be pleased to be privy to this bit of grandfatherly wisdom, or just a bit resentful at the gratuitous criticism of that paragon of "rat" terriers, my cousin's dog, Trixie.

It's unfortunately true that one's meetings with the barn owl are seldom very satis-

43

factory. He stays close to his roosting place by day, seldom showing himself except at night. The confrontation is apt to be fleeting and a little weird, for no matter how dark the evening the light under-parts—including the undersides of the wings—mark his wavering flight like a fluttering shroud.

There was one summer, however, when I was in my middle teens and becoming more ornithologically minded, that I had a number of opportunities to observe the barn owl. Kenny and I thought we would do some subcontracting for a mutual cousin, Ronald, who was in the pigeon business. This cousin,

only twelve-years-old but already a practiced horsetrader and small businessman, would contract to rid long-suffering farmers of their pigeon pests. Under cover of night, climbing among the beams and studs of their barns like an agile second-story man, he would "shine" the roosting or nesting pigeons with a flashlight and thrust the sleepy birds into a gunny sack slung over his shoulder. He charged a small fee for this service, but his real profit came from the sale of the birds to a poulterer in Cincinnati.

Down the road from us was the Henry Thompson farm with a huge barn full of

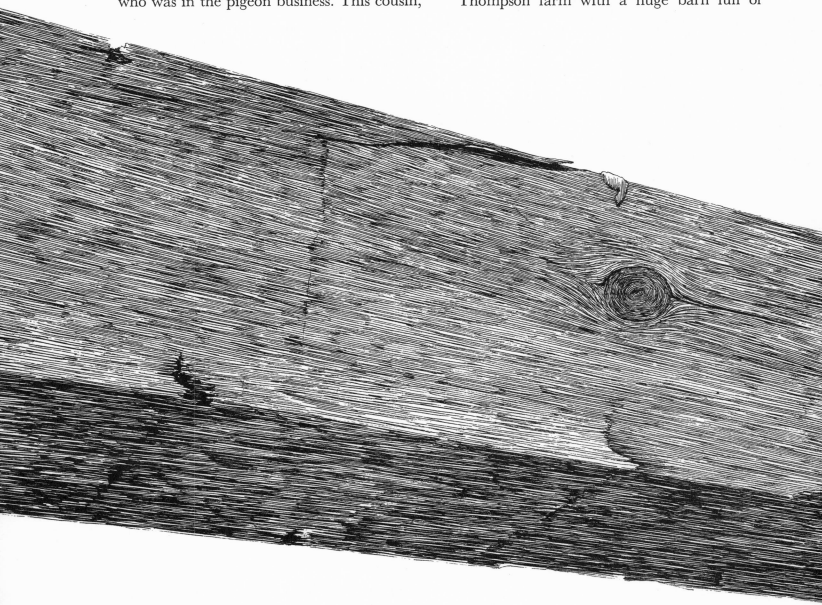

promise, its hay port wheeling with pigeons. But when we finally got around to our business we discovered very few pigeons roosting on the crossbeams and many empty nests that should have held squabs under the eaves. It was very mystifying. A few days later I made a daylight reconnaissance and noted very few birds flying about or perched on the roof peak. My investigation led me to take a look in the top of an ill-smelling but now unused silo and there, on the loading platform near the top, I saw a nesting barn owl and his mate. The birds seemed hospitable enough, for they scarcely moved, but I was a startled guest and quickly withdrew. I remember the hot tightening of fright in my chest as I scampered down. But I returned on several occasions later, first to observe the owls, then their eggs, and finally the ascending stairsteps of four owlets of different ages. By the time the last of four eggs had hatched, the first owlet seemed twice the size of his downy, late-arriving nest mate.

I was sure I had found the pigeon-hunter, but was not knowledgeable enough then to study the pellets which covered the platform and the bottom of the silo. And besides, at that time I did not know that owls regurgitate the fur, feathers, and bones of their prey; I mistook the pellets for manure. Those who know the barn owl well say that although pellet and stomach analysis show occasional bird remains, including pigeons, the barn owl will regularly nest in close proximity to pigeons and other birds without allowing such potential prey to divert them from their preference for rodents.

I remember clearly how long-legged these owls were. Their stilt-like legs seemed longer because they are lightly and smoothly feathered. But the chief memory of these close-ups is that of the heart-shaped facial disks and of this owl's long-nosed look. His expression is cat-like, self-contained, and secretive.

While the barn owl is most often seen about old buildings and abandoned houses, he nests in a surprising variety of places, including even old groundhog burrows, holes and apertures in old quarries, cliff faces, unused wells and mine shafts. The barn owl nests any time from April to September and differs from other owls in this domestic habit. My barn owls in the Hoosier silo were raising their brood during the dog days of August. I remember because my cousin and I had planned to combine business with bait hunting in our planned depredations on the pigeons. In August's dry spell the fishing worms were hard to find and we sometimes used pigeon meat for bait.

The barn owl ranges from the Gulf to the Canadian border, but you have a better chance of seeing him in the more southerly part of his haunts. He is a voracious feeder on the cotton rat in the southern portion of his range; a pocket gopher hunter in California. But the barn owl will find his rodent prey wherever he occurs. Mr. Alexander Sprunt, Jr. in his book *North American Birds of Prey* reports on the barn owl's success as a rodent hunter in the most unlikely places. He says: "A pair of barn owls once nested in a tower of the Smithsonian Institution building in Washington. Dr. A. K. Fisher made a study of 200 pellets (disgorged indigestible

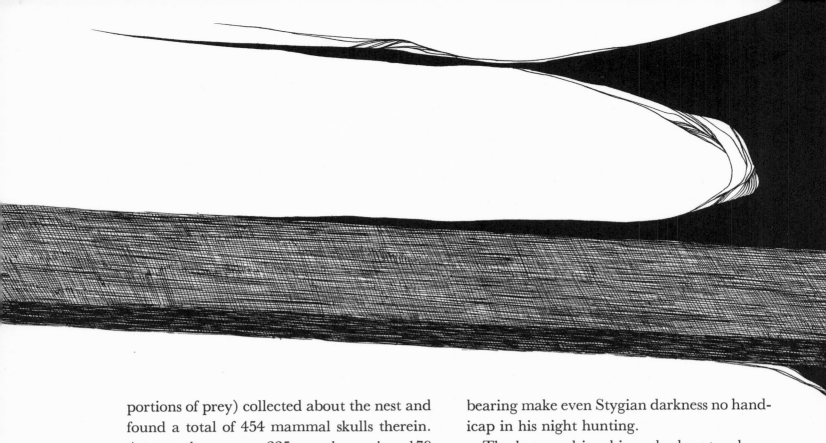

portions of prey) collected about the nest and found a total of 454 mammal skulls therein. Among them were 225 meadow mice, 179 house mice, 20 rats, and 20 shrews—an amazing collection for a pair of owls living in the heart of America's capital city."

The owlets are most demanding of their parents, and are said to eat their own weight in food in a single night. T. G. Wheelock reported that in one twenty-five minute period, twenty-one rodents were brought into a nest—sixteen mice, three gophers, a squirrel, and a rat—by the busy parents.

R. Payne's study of the barn owl's use of his asymmetrical ears as a tool for locating his prey is discussed on page 12. The owl's keen eyesight and sensitive triangulating bearing make even Stygian darkness no handicap in his night hunting.

The barn owl is a big owl, almost as large as a crow. His long legs and slim overall contours make him seem bigger than a barred owl. He is much larger than the screech owl and somewhat larger than the short-eared owl. He sometimes hunts the open fields and wet areas just as the short-eared owl does. Both of these birds show light underparts as they course their hunting grounds, but short-eared owls have a blunter, shorter-necked look than barn owls. And of course one regularly sees the short-eared owl patrolling such areas in the daylight. The barn owl confines his hunting to the night. He is a most satisfactory night bird.

THE ELF OWL

A number of obliging friends of mine in Arizona who know of my interest in owls have attempted to show me this true miniature owl, but I have consistently been jinxed. I have seen the nesting sites in old woodpecker holes in the sequaro cactus, but the tiny bird itself has eluded me save for my view of him in museum mountings. An owl the size of a house sparrow and little larger than a chickadee is an elf of an owl indeed. Very limited in range, the elf owl is confined to two general areas: the Texas elf owl to the lower Rio Grande valley and southward into Mexico, and the Whitney elf owl to southern Arizona, southwest New Mexico and south-

east California in a very restricted area of the lower Colorado River.

Mr. Frank Dobie once told me that this tiny owl, which seems to be exclusively a hunter of insects, sometimes had been seen by him around night campfires, beckoned there probably because of the light's attraction for insects. The little owl is apparently strictly nocturnal and feeds on moths, grasshoppers, various beetles, crickets, and centipedes. The little bird ranges up to elevations of a mile or more above sea level.

Smaller even than the pygmy owl, indeed the very smallest of all our owls, the elf is easily identified both as to locale and size. It is a gray-brown bird with darker mottled spots as well as light reddish specks on the upper parts. Its breast is buffily streaked. Its pale facial disks give the effect of white "eyebrows" on the bird, and there is also a butterfly shaped white area at the chin, outlined on its outer edges with black. Its eyes are yellow and its beak light colored. For its length, only five and a half to six and a half inches, it has an unusually wide wingspread, fourteen or fifteen to sixteen inches.

THE BARRED OWL

Roy Smith's one room camp, a reasonably large, peeled-cedar cabin, overlooked a low and smooth rock slope that descended gracefully to the waters of the west bay of Horseshoe Lake, Ontario. It was surrounded by a few spruce, hemlocks, firs, and birches; it squatted comfortably with a low seemliness, as if Frank Lloyd Wright had designed and implanted it on the one spot where it belonged. Its low peaked roof had an overhang at the front to shield a man who, on a mean, rainy day might have to get into the large bread box nailed on the front wall. The roof was made of corrugated metal, canoed and portaged in awkward sheets. It had been chosen over tarpaper because in the long run it would save time, labor, and money. And, besides, it was bear-proof.

At night, when the Coleman gas lanterns had finally blinked out their last diminishing light, but had given one some illumination between the turning-off and the ignominious scrabbling to wriggle into a sleeping bag, a man would huddle with anticipation. A deep silence would come on, broken only by the slow fizz of a dying fire in the wood range. Then, in a matter of seconds, the welcome blackness would bring out the white-footed mice that had gratefully moved in with us to share our grub. Welcome though these little large-eared beauties were as companions, they were troublesome too (as when they left their tracks in the carelessly uncovered butter), and we tried to reduce their number with traps baited with butter and oatmeal. Because of this fact we were always

careful not to make a mink set too close to the cabin lest we catch the "camp weasel" who invariably showed up after a day or two to advantage himself of the fine mouse supply. In the dying light of evening I often watched his camera-shutter movements as he raced in and out of the spaces of the wood-piles. Sometimes we'd hear his hunts in the cabin after dark. A wild, noisy race of scramblings and then a high, abruptly stopped squeak of the little victim would tell the tale. There would be silence again, then more tiny furry sounds of the rummaging mice and soon, when the weasel had cached his first mouse somewhere outside the camp, he would return to take another. The camp weasel was a far better mouse hunter than we were mouse trappers.

But night sounds came from outside the cabin as well. One November night we heard the barking hoots of the barred owl and the sound was so loud we thought the owl must be quite close. The hoots were very different from the booming hoos of a great horned owl far down the lake. A few evenings later in the weak glow of the waning daylight I flushed the round-headed gray bird as I hurried toward the warm cabin from the chilly discomfort of the log outhouse. All I saw was the flat, level trajectory of the gliding owl after he flapped heavily from his perch and sailed away in a low, smooth, and silent glide through the second growth.

So, the influx of mice at our camp had beckoned a second mouser. Unfortunately, once the owl took up residence near us, we lost the services of the camp weasel. Although the white-foot supply seemed inexhaustible,

the weasel's visits ceased and I concluded that the slim, swift four-footed mouser had himself been picked up by the two-footed one, the barred owl.

In the evenings after we had returned from the trapline or from a day's hunting I began to search out this owl's feeding roost. A lucky discovery of a half dozen pellets helped me to locate one perch in a big hemlock a hundred yards back in the bush from the cabin. I spotted the owl fairly regularly during that three week period. He was usually perched on a limb quite close to the bole of the hemlock where he suffered me to observe him.

One night as I lay in the top bunk of the silent, pitch-dark cabin, I heard a dull thump on the corrugated roof directly above my head and not three feet away. The creature was undoubtedly a flying squirrel that had glided to a noisy landing on the roof from some high limb that had served him as a launching pad. I listened a moment to the scratchy bumpings and scurryings of the squirrel. Then suddenly there was silence and as suddenly a soft brush of wings on the metallic surface followed instantly by the loud anguished squeal from the squirrel. Then silence again. I held my breath and listened for further evidence of the little tragedy out there in the dark, but the owl had evidently plucked the flat-bodied squirrel from the roof and made off on moth-silent wings without a formal landing. I lay there scarcely daring to breathe for the closeness of the violent drama had raised my own neck hackles. As I dozed off I visualized "my" barred owl perched on the limb of his feeding station beheading the hapless flying squirrel.

For some reason a particular barred owl remains freshest in my memory. I observed this owl in the dense, green cover of a spruce swamp in New Brunswick. It was broad daylight, even sunny, with the open places making a strong contrast to the dark shadows of the spruces. The barred owl was perched, however, so the soft reflected light gave a perfect view of his field marks—the large size (he is our fourth largest owl) and the overall chunky robustness of the bird. The owl's large head sits atop a barred ruff that gives him an obese, double-chinned look. The general impression is one of gray rather than the brownness that characterized the great horned owl. And of course the round headed barred owl is "earless." The "chins" are narrowly barred cross-wise, and the breast and belly are boldy streaked lengthwise on the buffy white background. The placement of bars and stripes is the very opposite from that of the great horned owl. The facial disks of the barred owl are distinctive, too, for they are concentrically ringed in black. The upper part of the barred owl is gray brown blotched with yellow white. Most of all I remember my owl's eyes. They were deep brown, large and spectral. The uniformly dark eyes, showing no pupil, are thoughtful, brooding, unfierce, and seemed even innocent in their deep contemplation of me. The barred owl has a canary yellow beak and strongly accented facial disks which give the bird a very impressive look. My New Brunswick owl watched me calmly and only moved by turning his head to follow me when I backed away. The encounter seemed quite a personal one; the barred owl was watching me too and seemed quite as aware of me as I was of him. I can never forget his great, luminous eyes and his seemingly careful examination of me as I stood below him and looked him in the face. I remember also that as I turned away I flushed a hen and cock spruce grouse not ten yards from the perching owl.

Next to the screech owl, this owl is the one most often seen. It prefers the woods but does live and breed in a variety of habitats, and its various sub-species have a wide range. The unearthly repertoire of cries that this owl can make has horrified, mystified and dismayed more people than that of any other owl. Unearthly screams and caterwauls of the barred owl have been the howling "wildcats" and "panthers" of many a bewildered imagination of those who have not had the benefit of experience with the fantastic versatility of the owl's cries. My good friend and hunting partner, Bill Gandall, met me at a previously selected old woods crossroads for lunch one day. During the morning I had heard the barred owl and was waiting for his comment, knowing as I did that Bill just might not know what had produced the crazy cacophony. There was no greeting from Bill, just a startled exclamation: "There must be some crazy people hunting in here," he said. "Did you hear those wild yells and wails? They must have dogs with them . . . or what was it?" His confusion was understandable, for the barred owl had put on one of the finest performances that I have ever heard from this seemingly demonic bird. As

a daytime vocalist (never mind the impact
when he is heard at night!) the barred owl
is superb at startling and confusing the innocent by his idiotic gabbles, squeals, screams,
and harsh, raucous mutterings. The jumble
of harsh consonants and gutturals, all in what
sounds like a crazed Welsh accent, seems
utterly arbitrary in its outlandish mixture.
It sounds like a battle to the death between
nameless, unimaginable demons. His cackling
and gabblings, his chuckles, barks, yells and
squallings, his maniacal laughter, his howls
and yowls, screams and screeches cannot be
written down. Although that morning I

jotted on the inside of a Hershey wrapper
one sequence of noises the bird made that I
can produce for whatever it may be worth.
On Monday, November 22, 1965 this particular barred owl was repeating (amongst
all the other wild idiotic cries) a noise that
can be written as uh-*huh* wee-ay-*ouk*. This
bird interspersed these wild squalls with his
regular eight hoots that has so often been
written "Who cooks for you? Who cooks for
you-all?"

This formal call of the barred owl is neat and systematic, indeed so generally consistent that he has been called the eight hooter. Hoo-hoo, hoo-hoo, hoo-hoo, hoo-hoo-aw (with the "aw" slurred downward). These mathematically spaced hoos, each discrete and specific coming in terse couplets, make a hoarse and resonant call. It reminds some of a foghorn. Once heard it is not too difficult to imitate.

In spite of its size this owl is not the versatile hunter that the great horned owl is. Richard Pough says in his *Audubon Bird Guide* "This owl is mild by comparison with the great horned. Its feet are small and weak and it seldom tackles large prey. Mice form the bulk of its food, but it eats other small mammals, frogs, crayfish, fish, insects, and birds. It apparently takes a good many smaller owls and any small bird it is lucky enough to catch." In the woods while he is hunting, the barred owl's flight is light and buoyant; its wingbeats are slow and methodical. But it is also adept in thick cover, turning and flapping and gliding through the timber and shrubs with apparent ease on its broad, somewhat stubby wings. This owl hunts the same cover frequented by red-shouldered hawks, forming another ecological pair as its cousin, the short-eared owl, forms with the marsh hawk.

This owl does not build a nest or even convert one. It lays its eggs, pure white and glossy, usually two to four in number, in hollow trees or sometimes in the nests of crows and hawks.

THE BURROWING OWL

The first time I saw this long-legged and seemingly knock-kneed owl was in 1929 in eastern South Dakota. It was standing on a broken-off fence post and it performed its comical bowing curtsy as if it had been programmed just to please this gawking Hoosier who had never seen one. The two species of the burrowing owl stay strictly to the plains country, the western variety ranging from British Columbia south and east to North and South Dakota, Nebraska, Kansas, eastern Colorado and west to California in the southern part of this range. According to Alexander Sprunt, Jr. the Florida burrowing owl inhabits the central prairie portions of this state and the Tampa region south to Sarasota and east of Lake Okeechobee.

The burrowing owl is true to its name for it does indeed live in burrows. Furthermore, while it does use the abandoned burrows of prairie dogs (where that fast-disappearing little rodent persists), it regularly digs its own. Those who have observed these little excavators at work say that both birds in the pair work at the task and use their feet for the job. The burrows drop a foot or so, then level off for half a dozen or more feet, ending in a chamber in which six or seven eggs are laid.

A Nebraskan friend of mine once drove me to a small colony of these owls. In an area that once had seen buffalo and prairie chickens, five pairs of these little owls had dug their burrows, a little colony under the grassy flats. The excavated earth made noticeable mounds at each burrow and the area around the den opening showed the fresh manure of these birds. We saw no owls but my friend stated that in the evenings he had seen the birds awing and heard their chattering "cak-cucking" as they flew. The burrowing owl, he said, also makes cuckoo-like calls that can be heard for a considerable distance.

This owl seldom takes birds but otherwise its diet is most varied. It eats all kinds of mice, ground squirrels, and gophers. Like other small owls it captures many beetles and

other insects and also preys upon lizards and snakes. Frogs and other aquatic creatures are taken when available.

The burrowing owl has distinct white eyebrows at the top of the facial disks over each yellow eye and a white mustache and "chin whiskers" below. He is gray brown, much mottled in white over the back and barred in brown on the lower breast and belly, and has small white spots over his round earless head. Since he is stubby-tailed and long-legged he gives a slightly awkward appearance. He is a bit bigger than a screech owl, and seems even larger when standing. He is actually nine to ten and a half inches in length with a wingspread of twenty-two to twenty-four inches.

THE HOME OF THE GREAT GRAY OWL

There is something quite wonderful about mountains above the timber line. When a man can at last command from open alpine slopes the vast stretches of timber that lie below him, he feels that he has achieved a freedom usually granted only to birds. When one gains these slopes that roll upwards in a succession of ascending horizons and can look down at last on the fine tips of ancient spruces, there comes a special sense of release. To gain that freedom one has trudged slowly up the ridges, dense with trees and undergrowth and relieved occasionally in sunny patches by a jackpot of blueberry patches. The mossy ground winks with the glossy leaves and shining globes of bearberries, crowberries, and low bush cranberries. One has felt oneself almost a prisoner of this dank growth, has sensed the accompanying half-fear of those places that alter but little with the passing years. The gloomy, only occasionally sunlit denseness seems a veritable tunnel of time, subtly foreboding because of this silent changelessness.

The wild fastness of the Brooks Range which sweeps across northern Alaska is a wilderness like this. It stretches for miles in rugged majesty as a shallow half-moon bowed toward the Arctic Circle, and it surveys the Arctic ocean across a wide stretch of tundra—sometimes, as at its eastern tip, from a distance of only fifty miles; sometimes, as near its center, it arises more than one hundred and fifty miles south of the Arctic prairie. The north slope of the Brooks is north of the timberline. Only scrub willows cling to its watercourses and other favored places. The other slope, draining far to the south into the Yukon basin, is timbered. The spruces reach silently to the skies along its lower ridges. They grow densely but very slowly in the short growing season of the sub-arctic. Sometimes a nine-inch-diameter tree will show three to four hundred annual rings.

A few sparse stands of birch and poplar may also be found. The softly carpeted slopes rise in long billows breaking finally against the crowning jumble of the rocky summits. These crowns rise in places to ten thousand feet in their highest reaches and they are more often than not "children's mountains," jagged, pointed, saw-toothed—classic drawings as from a childish hand. The wildest of them rise to the west of the upper Alatna River; they are the grim, toothy Arregetches, their sharp peaks fearful as a shark's maw, their fangs darkened and stained above the shaggy spruces.

Once, on a bright blue October day in the foothills of the Arregetches, I sat just above the timberline with the clear Alatna flowing below me, glassing the sides of the opposing range. By my side was a spotting scope, its crystal Cyclops eye mounted on a tripod. Far below me was the dense spruce fringe of the river, a scraggly area perhaps fifty yards wide. Beyond it lay a half mile flat of knee-high scrub willow, bordered on the right by the similarly timbered flanks of the Kutuk which empties into the Alatna a quarter mile below. These open clearings remain after massive avalanches of snow and dirt have swept the slopes, shearing away the trees and leaving a giant matchstick jumble at their bottoms. I was looking for bears, for at that time of year the barren ground grizzly is drawn to the long narrow scars of the landslides where vetch grows in the clearings. The great bears dig the gleaming white nitrogenous roots of this mountain pea, their system seeming to favor this succulent fare at this time of year.

The day before, my companion and friend, Harmon Helmericks, bush pilot and woodsman nonpareil, and I had watched a grizzly bear dig for roots on these very slides. Under the magnification of the thirty power spotting scope, the grizzly seemed almost in our laps. We could see clearly the color of his coat, mahogany brown over his sides and legs, lighter over his hump and head where the sun had burned him a creamy honey dun. The vagaries of the mountain air currents waved his long fur in dreary undulations like the rolling surface of a wind-stirred Kansas wheat field.

I saw no bears the next day but I watched a huge bull moose, whose rutting wallows we had seen (and smelled) the day before in the Kutuk's bottom. While my companion far below me was packing our duffel at an old dirt-floored cabin he had once built and wintered in, I was tolling the bull into the spruce below me by simulating the coughing grunts of a rival bull and the seductive lowing moans of the cow. Later Bud Helmericks got movie footage of that eager bull. But somehow I remember the occasion not for the close view of the bull moose, but for two brief views I had of another, even rarer, denizen of those wild mountain reaches.

As I made my way down from my perch above timber into the upper edge of the spruces, I flushed a huge gray bird. His size astounded me and for a moment I thought I had seen another golden eagle. But in my eagerness to get back to my companion to report the bull's availability for pictures, I allowed the episode to recede. My excitement over the moose had dulled at first the full

import of this rival experience. But luck was with me that day, for a bit farther down I saw the great bird again. He was perched in sober dignity in the middle branches of a sparse spruce. This time I realized what a rare chance it really was. I stopped and looked him in the eye at twenty-five or thirty yards. His huge facial disks were barred in concentrically smaller circles toward his yellow eyes. He tipped his head to one side in solemn scrutiny and then took off. I vividly remember feeling that this was surely the most scholarly-looking of all owls.

His course brought him somewhat closer to me as he picked an opening through the trees. His body appeared huge, and the vast spread and the great width of those silent wings made him seem even more out of proportion in this dense environment. His wing beat was slow and powerful and unhurried. He turned his head toward me as he flew by and then he passed heavily into the growth. It was only later, after we had paddled silently across the Alatna and had located and photographed our bull moose, that I could fully appreciate the privilege I had had. Although I have never seen another— and I have been within his range in Alaska, the Yukon, Quebec and Labrador on other occasions—I had seen the great gray owl. I can never forget him.

Those who have seen him plucked of his deep, fluffy plumage say his body is smaller in size and weight than that of either the great horned or the snowy owl, but you can be sure that when *you* first see him he will appear even larger than either of these two large owls. His long tail contributes notice-

ably to his body length of two to two and one-half feet, which is roughly a full half-foot longer than the average great horned owl. But it is the breadth and spread of his wings— fifty-four to sixty inches—that surprises one. Five feet is a great span for a bird whose top weight is perhaps two and one-half to three pounds, the weight of a small frying chicken. And it is his oversized head—a round dome without ear tufts—that increases his seeming hugeness. His fluffy head measures twenty inches in circumference, and his professional mien is heightened by the huge facial disks, each of which may measure six inches.

The great gray owl is a rodent hunter that is also capable of taking the snowshoe hare, the "bread of the woods" in the great north. One observer found that one of these owls had, after beheading a red squirrel, swallowed the remainder whole. The great gray probably takes ptarmigan when he can manage, and Dr. A. K. Fisher reported that a colleague of his had taken "no less than thirteen skulls and other remains of redpoll linnets from the stomach of a single bird." Dr. Fisher reported that he himself had examined one stomach that contained a small bird, seven mice, and the remains of four other unidentified small mammals.

This owl breeds and lives in the timbered fastness from Labrador across Canada to Alaska. He is an occasional, but very occasional, winter visitor to the northern United States. But don't count on adding the great gray owl to your life list without traveling north, and even then you must be lucky, for he is truly a rare bird even in his northern range.

72

THE SAW WHET OWL

In the Adirondacks it is still winter in late March and a fire in the fireplace is always welcome. On a particular March night in 1953, my wife and I were reading before the fire and the only sounds were an occasional swishing as one of us turned a page and the light hissing of the poplar logs. Suddenly, just outside the window at my back, came an unearthly sound. It was the more eerie because it was unidentifiable. It was not the sound of bird or beast; it was mechanical, harsh, metallic; and it was weak but very definitely raucous. It seemed man-made, and what man would be out in that cold wintry night?

"Scree-aw, scree-aw," it came again, and this time the sound identified itself. Few people have heard the saw whet owl, and in our times as few have heard a man sharpen a saw, but the sound is unmistakable,

and the call of this little owl sounds almost exactly like a metal file pushed across the teeth of this tool.

With some excitement, for it was the first of these little owls either of us had seen or heard, we armed ourselves with a flashlight and "shined" the little owl perched on a limb near the bole of a veteran elm. Seemingly undisturbed by the light, this owl, known as being "absurdly tame," according to Roger Tory Peterson, allowed us to watch him until we were too chilled to continue our examination.

A year or so later I was fortunate enough to get a good close-up view of this owl when one became lodged temporarily behind the

YOUNG SAW WHET OWLS

chicken wire screen inside a window in an old sugaring-off house that had once been converted into a chicken house. His round head (the saw whet has no ear tufts) and rather shallow face looked out at us without alarm. Considering his predicament, his big yellow eyes had a rather complacent look. I went to the shed for an old parrot cage thinking to hold the little bird for a day or two, but when I returned he had chinned his way up and over the screening and was gone.

Although the saw whet owl is widely distributed across the northern parts of the country wherever its favorite woodlands are available, it is seldom seen because of its shy habits. It is certainly more often heard than seen, a characteristic situation with most owls, but few who are not familiar with this lovely little bird would identify the raspy two syllable whistle. The saw whet also makes a low cooing whistle, "too-too-too," which is sometimes repeated with the same monotony of the whipporwill's call, as many as a hundred times in succession.

The saw whet owl is noticeably smaller than the robin in overall length, but like his larger cousin among the small owls, the screech owl, this little owl is surprisingly fierce with prey species. With its seven to eight inch size one would hardly think it could kill the common pigeon, yet it has

been reliably reported as doing so. Its regular diet consists chiefly of mice, but it also takes chipmunks, flying squirrels, shrews, and other small mammals.

The smallest of the eastern owls, the saw whet has a wingspread of a foot and a half to twenty-two inches. Audubon called it the Acadian owl. Its fluffy feathering, relatively large wingspread, and large head give the saw whet the illusion of being a bigger bird. Actually it is an inch or two smaller than the screech owl and a full two inches smaller than the robin. Its large rounded and earless head is streaked with white and its upper parts are brown occasionally spotted with white. Its white breast is strongly streaked with heavy brown stripes and its blunt tail is crossed by four or five thin white bars. The gray facial disks of the saw whet owl are less distinct than those, for example, of the Richardson's owl.

Tree hollows, old flicker holes, and especially the dens of hairy woodpeckers make the usual nests for these owls. The hen lays from four to seven white, smooth eggs.

THE GREAT HORNED OWL

Even his name carries weight and a feeling of dignity and influence, as well as an impressive sense of power. He is indeed "great" and—along with the snowy owl—one of the largest owls. He is "horned" and somehow his ear tufts seem at times to be the surrogate horns of the devil himself. Great . . . horned . . . and all owl is this feathered king of the woods. Arthur Bent calls him "the tiger of the woods"; another writer describes him as "awesomely fierce and powerful, nemesis of a host of prey species" including birds as large as grouse and crows, goshawks and red-tailed hawks, mammals from mice, squirrels and hares to other even larger animals that outweigh him several times, animals on the order of skunks, opossums, woodchucks and a variety of aquatic creatures and snakes. A very generalized feeder is the great horned owl.

Although he will nest and hunt close to human settlement, as long as there are stands of big timber nearby, he is only fully at home in the wilderness. Deep pine, hemlock, or spruce, broken by hardwoods and bordered by swamps and lakes, are his ideal habitat. A late-winter hiker in the northern parts of our country may see the nest of this owl looming large in the bare top of some tree. As they are early nesters, these owls often set their eggs when the body of a parent bird must protect the eggs from a late snowfall.

And once the downy and voracious young are born, the parent birds become hunting machines fetching to the owlets a veritable cornucopia of game. The great horned owl is the generalized feeder he is because he is physically able to pick and choose. He and especially she, for the hen is larger than the cock, tends to be most catholic of all owls in his tastes.

When you first set eyes on one of these owls you sense that you are somehow in the presence of an equal. His stare is almost one of regal condescension. He moves but little, taking off in flight only if you push your investigations. I have always thought of him as a condottiere among predators whose prowess had at last given him a princely domain. To me this is our most impressive bird of prey.

This great bird is often referred to by the sentimental as "savage," "vicious," or as "a ruthless killer." All of these terms are of course anthropomorphic, presumably reflecting some kind of claim of human superiority on the matter of violence. In fact, the bird is merely an effective hunter and hardly deserves criticism from a species that can scarcely make it in good conscience. This owl is an effective hunter partly because of his great power and size and partly because of his nocturnal prowlings when, as a night feeder, he has the advantage of darkness which adds mightily to his success.

Just as the short-eared owl hunts at late afternoon and evening the same ground coursed over by the marsh hawk during the day, so the great horned owl hunts by evening and by night the same thick cover watched from the perch of the red-tailed hawk by day. The two hunters prey on many of the same rodents. The owl courses the night woods on silent wings in search of food, but he also watches for game from a perch. Once, while tending muskrat traps from a canoe on a sluggish Ontario stream that wound its way through a marsh studded by muskrat "push-ups," I spotted this owl watching for 'rats from a naked, November alder. When our approach finally unnerved him, the big bird took off in powerful strokes, the leading edges of his broad wings beating so strongly on the lattice of branches that they made a great clatter and broke off a shower of dry, dead twigs. He made off silently once he had cleared the thicket and disappeared into the dark green gloom of a spruce swamp that bordered the marsh.

Often, horned owls are shot by professional trappers because they *are* deadly muskrat hunters. Indeed this owl often poaches on the trapper's line, and once I saw evidence that this owl had waded out into six inches of water to retrieve a muskrat that he had partly eaten from the same trap three days before. The horned owl is known to catch fish by wading and seizing bottom feeders such as bullhead and suckers when they come into shallow water.

As a generalized feeder, the horned owl displays an impartial selection that even includes other predatory birds. The literature is filled with reports of this owl's predation on other owls. Many a barred owl, itself a sizeable predator, falls victim to the larger owl, and the same literature is sprinkled with good evidence that roosting red-tails are seized on their perches and, in spite of their large size, killed and eaten when disadvantaged by darkness and sleep. Even turkeys and domestic chickens are sometimes taken, and several observers who have seen the act itself tell an eerie tale of the owl's alighting near the victim and crowding it off its roost as a preliminary to the kill. Indeed, horned owls hunt in all manners and methods, from seizing their victims on the wing, to perching and watching to wading, and even walking in search of their prey.

The versatility of this owl's hunting methods is shown by an experience related by Mr. Walter Edmonds, the novelist, who is a devoted naturalist and a keen observer of birds and animals as well as of men. On his farm on the edge of the Adirondacks in New York state he had a pen of hens and pullets, the chicken house surrounded by a high wire fence. The outlet from the house to the hen-yard was a slanting ramp. The hens began to disappear, and finally Mr. Edmond's farmer and he concluded that a raccoon was making the nightly raids on the roosting hens. It seemed unlikely that even a good climber like the gray fox could manage the high wire fencing, and there was no sign of digging under the fence and no other means of entry to the hens. A trap set on the ramp produced the very next night a huge great horned owl. Somehow the picture of this winged hunter alighting in the chicken yard and then marching afoot up the ramp and through the low opening to its victims gave the whole episode a macabre atmosphere which would not have been felt had the kills been made in the expected manner. The

vision of this waddling executioner stepping in measured stride up the ramp (the entry hold was too small for him to have flown directly into the roosting area) to select from the perch a favored victim has always had for me a kind of grim, medieval horror. It has added to my admiration for this efficient hunter, who wades in half a foot of water or walks with the march of fate up a ramp to reach its intended prey.

The sight of this owl hunting from a perch is not easily forgotten. Once, while returning by canoe from the trapline of an Ontario trapper friend, my wife and I noticed a red squirrel running first along the rocky shore and then along accommodating drifting wood on the water's edge. At the same moment we noticed a horned owl perched atop a dead white birch stump a few feet back and above the shore. We ceased paddling at once and both noted afterwards how much like an extension of that ten foot stump the bird appeared. As the unsuspecting squirrel approached, the owl humped its shoulders and lowered its head preparatory to its stoop to seize the squirrel. Just before the moment of truth it must have noticed an inadvertent movement on the part of one of us, for the great bird took off in alarm with a swelling of body and wings which my wife described as looking almost like a hot air balloon suddenly cut loose from its moorings. It was less a flight than an ascent, she said. Once in the air the owl flapped heavily to the cover of the timber and, luckily, we located it again as we made our way down the lake. He sat perched high in a tall cedar and watched us pass with a calm rotation of his head. It was

all we could do to keep our friend from trying a shot with his .30-30 at that "desperate rat poacher and partridge killer," as he called him.

Trappers and guides point out, and in two instances I have confirmed this myself, that they have never handled a horned owl without smelling skunk odor on him. Both horned owls that I have seen in traps smelled strongly of skunk, so it is clear that in certain areas at least, this owl hunts the skunk regularly as one of his prey species. Once in the wintry, dark green gloom of an Ontario spruce swamp I saw the spot where an owl had killed and eaten a skunk on the snow. The skunk, whose only defense does not daunt the great horned owl, had been seized just a few feet from where his shredded remains were found. The sweep of the owl's wing primaries could be traced in the soft snow, revealing how the silent hunter had mantled his victim, propping and bracing himself with his five foot wingspread while he tightened his grip and drove his talons into the victim's

chest cavity. The skunk had thrown his scent, but to no avail. He had waddled a few feet in a half circle of desperation, but had succumbed not ten feet from where the owl had first struck him.

Grossman and Hamlet in their fine book, *Birds of Prey of the World*, show a remarkable sequence of color photographs of a great horned owl killing a large black snake.

The great horned owl when perched is quickly identifiable by his brownness, his great size (larger than a crow, from 18″ to 25″ in length), and by his "ear" tufts or "horns." His big yellow eyes start out of a light brown facial disk that is edged with black. His eyes are partly covered on their inner edges by the V of his forehead. His neck and upper breast are white. Above and below this white area beneath his black beak are dark brown, almost black, lengthwise stripes. Beneath these he is darkly and narrowly cross-barred in dark brown over the whitish background. These feathers and the white stripes are neat and seemingly compact

while the feathers in the white chin area seem made up of large, almost fluffy feathers. His short and rounded tail is barred.

Few observers of the owl, who have seen him flying soundlessly through the evergreens, do not suppress a slight shudder bordering on fear. No wonder grouse so often roost tight against the bole of a tree in the closest cover as protection against this brown spectre. In his various sub-species there is some variation in coloration, especially in the Arctic variety, which is often pale almost to whiteness.

This owl's wings may spread from forty-eight to fifty-five inches and seem even larger because of their great width. In flight one does not notice the ear tufts; they are quite prominent, though, on the perched bird.

An old crow's nest, or that of a red-tailed hawk or heron, located high in a tree will hold from two to three white eggs. Occasionally this owl will nest on overhanging ledges, caves, hollow trees, and such. Again, as with other owl species, the younger are born in "stairsteps," as the eggs do not hatch simultaneously. The largest of three dirty gray nestlings may appear noticeably bigger than his last, late-arriving sibling. But all are continuously hungry, and hunting for their young is a heavy chore for the parent birds.

The hemlock-nesting owls I observed in the late winter and early spring woods of the Adirondacks found the high population of the snowshoe rabbit that particular year much to their liking. A scatter of the hind legs of their favorite prey beneath the nesting tree gave a strong indication of the menu. The "good luck pieces" meant bad luck that winter to many a hare huddled in his form, or hollowed-out nest. These same owls took a heavy toll also of the numerous red squirrels. Their two-to-three-inch-long pellets revealed in their dense, felt-like packing numerous skulls of mice and feathers of birds.

In the chapter on the calls of owls the reader can "listen" to the hoots of the great horned owl. Here let it suffice to say that he is known sometimes as the five hooter. The hoots of the horned owls, unlike the sharp distinctive hooting of the barred owl, have a sonorous booming timber. At times, the awed listener striving to locate the position of a hooting horned owl will feel that the sound reverberates from within his own head. The hollow, soft, booming hoos are ventriloquistic, and the more eerie for seeming so. Those unfamiliar with owls may easily take the low soft hoo-hoo-hooooo-hoo-hoo as the soulful baying of a distant hound. But the sound has great carrying power.

THE SHORT-EARED OWL

In Indiana in the days before the combine, which mows and threshes wheat in one operation, the grain was first cut with a binder that spewed out twine-tied sheaves that were stacked into "shocks" so the grain heads could cure and dry. Later these bundles were pitch-forked on wagons and trundled to a separator powered by a steam engine that threshed the grain. For a period between shocking and threshing the fields stood bare with their stubble decorated by the irregularly spaced shocks. These shocks became nesting havens for a vast population of mice and rats.

In the evenings my cousin Kenny and I were sent for the cows, a daily but pleasant chore that small boys performed on midwestern farms in those days. A dusty, tracked lane led to the woodlot with its windmill and water trough and connecting field where the cows found shade, water and clover. The dust of this lane was deep and cool to our bare feet in the grass-divided tracks. Some years, wheat fields would border us all the way to the cows, and those years instructed us in the habits of the short-eared owls. In the evening light we could observe the coursing of one or two of these fine mousers as they patrolled the stubble and wheat shocks beneath their low level flight. Often we would observe their uneven wingbeats, interspersed with the air-treading, hovering tactics, and some evenings we would see the successful termination of a hunt. A hapless mouse, crawling and tumbling among the bearded grain heads, was usually the victim. The wobbly, moth-like flutter of the short-eared owl's flight would suddenly stop for a few seconds of hovering. Then the motion would turn into a graceful stoop when the owl dropped on his prey. Now the wings

would be raised high over the bird's head, their tips pointing skyward, spilling the air to speed the descent of his down-and-forward-reaching taloned feet. The pickup was light and airy. Sometimes, however, the victim was the larger-bodied rat, and in such an instance there was usually a tussle, a scrabbling fight on the shock top until the owl's talons had penetrated the rat's rib cavity. The short-eared owl is a late afternoon and evening hunter, often coursing the same areas that are hunted earlier in the day by the marsh hawk.

This owl is surprisingly widely distributed, and one may see it over open areas, marshes, dunes and meadows (both natural and man-made) from the stubbles of sugar cane fields as far south as Louisiana, where it is a winter visitor, to the tundra lands of Arctic Alaska and Canada. The short-eared owl even nests in the Arctic, and a considerable seasonal migration there is widely reported. I once saw a short-eared owl perched on the low stump of a water-killed striped maple sapling in a beaver meadow in Ontario and later saw this owl, or another like it, coursing over the grassy border of the same beaver pond.

This bird flew low over the grass tops and interspersed his flight with short glides that sometimes were punctuated by characteristic hovering and treading air with rapidly beating wings. The short-eared owl usually appears quite earless in flight; indeed he seems singularly blunt-headed and bull-necked when observed over his favorite terrain. This owl not only hunts such open areas but roosts and nests there as well. A mid-morning stroll will often flush the short-eared owl out of the grasses of open meadows, marshes or from the standing grain in wheat fields.

My most vivid memories of the short-eared owl are from Kansas and Alberta. Once in July, just after the seemingly boundless wheat fields of Kansas had been combined, and later in Alberta in October after the later harvesting season there, my family and I watched large numbers of these owls hunt the stubble for their favorite prey, the mouse.

One July evening in Kansas, we pulled our car off on the shoulder of Route 66, alighted and watched six or eight of these owls glide, flap and hover over an area that must have harbored a particularly large population of mice. The owls put on quite

an aerial ballet that evening and we may have interrupted a nuptial flight, for high rises, swooping, and air treading seemed mixed with the more mundane hunting tactics.

The flat, straw-strewn stubble made a golden monochrome vista which was broken only by a distant grain elevator that loomed above a village far down the string-straight pavement. The evening sun sharpened the fine lines and planes of the simple but elegant structure and etched it cleanly against the blue Kansas sky. Short-eared owls always remind me of that evening in Kansas.

This owl, like the snowy owl, also will hunt from a low perch. A post, rock, hummock or a low stub in the open may reveal one, sitting motionless and with cat-like vigilance, watching for a mouse or vole to reveal itself. The short-eared is a brown owl with a light, pale buffy breast. It is mottled brown on its back, and streaked longitudinally but sparsely on its breast, more heavily striated on its breast than on its belly. Its facial disks are not very distinctive, but its eyes are encircled with black and this dark area sets off both the light "mustache" and the startlingly yellow eyes. In flight this owl is distinctive not only for the heavy, seemingly peckless head, but also for a dark spot on the under surface of the wings and a light spot on the upper surface. The ear tufts are hardly noticeable even when the bird is seen on its perch. This is a fair-sized owl, smaller than a crow but ranging from thirteen to seventeen inches in length. It has a wingspread of thirty-eight to forty-four inches.

The nest, although on the ground, is not easy to find. The one short-eared nest that I observed was hidden in the shelter of a weedy tussock. It was only slightly hollowed out and was lined with dried grass and a sprinkling of feathers, presumably its own, since this owl kills few birds. The eggs, usually six or seven in number, are white. Unfortunately the short-eared nest I observed was raided by a crow or skunk and the eggs destroyed. The female did not lay another clutch of eggs, at least not in that nest, although I continued to see her and her mate in the area.

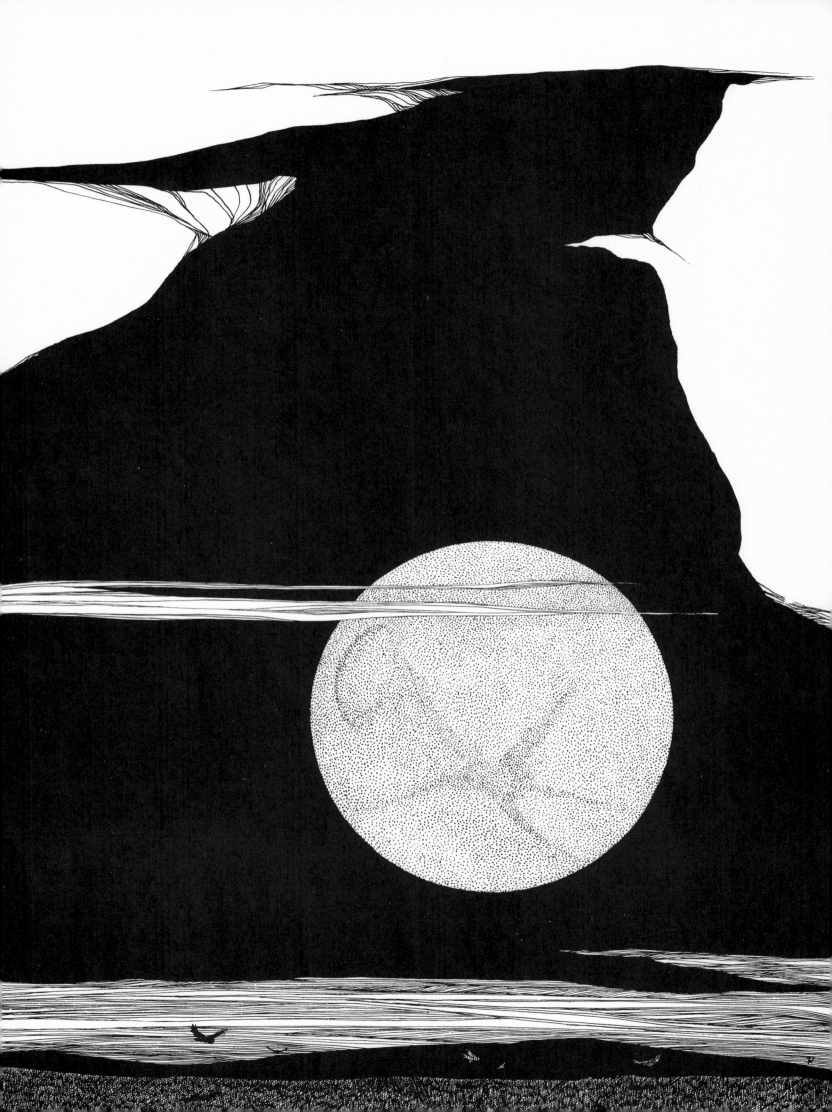

Early on in this collaboration I made a request of Peter Parnall. "In two cases, Pete," I said, "I would like to have you draw owls in settings of my own choosing." One of these was this drawing for the hawk owl, and I wanted a particular scene because of a debt I wished to discharge to one of my favorite mentors. I think it makes a nice owl story, this tale about one of the most unlikely owls of all American owls, the hawk owl.

Peter willingly obliged me, so what you see above is the artist's re-creation of a scene of a lonely old barn in Ontario in late November, 1956. That country has the exquisite remoteness of classical "spruce-moose" country: low ridges, often bald to the ancient stone on their tops, and lightly timbered on their flanks with second growth hardwood—

92

THE HAWK OWL AND ROGER TORY PETERSON

elegant birches, popples, and striped maple, the latter often scarred by the neatly-spaced stripping marks of the moose's lower mandibles. Between the ridges are small spruce swamps, dark, gloomy, and wet with old rotting trunks and with sphagnum and *Cladonia*, that lichen so colorfully misnamed "caribou moss." Around these dark green conclaves of the hardy spruce are clearings of bear grass and buckbrush, and often fringing the swamps stand the graying, lonely old spires of tall dead spruces. They are called "shakos" in that country.

My wife, Sheila, and I were walking these ridges one gray day, searching the country for moose, expecting at any moment to see the great dark forms leisurely crossing the muskegs, standing silently in the swamp

fringe, or feeding on the ridge sides, for the rut was on and the moose had been unusually active during the day. We had come down off a ridge together, our separate routes having converged where the higher ground tapered down into the bottoms. Our eyes were drawn upward by the gaunt pointing finger of a tall, isolated shako. On its tip was the silhouette of a perched bird. His command of his surroundings was unique; the whole silent stretch of marsh and ridge lay below him. He didn't look like an owl, and indeed he never does. His tail bobbed up and down, not with the seeming mechanical purposefulness of a phoebe's tail but more half-heartedly, more absent-mindedly. His contours confused me, for he had the rounded head of an owl but the long tail and stance of a hawk. I moved slowly around to get what little light there was at my back, and when I did I could make out the sharp barrings on his breast and belly. As I say, his stance was hawk-like; he perched at an angle to the vertical. He had none of the quiet, upright dignity of the owl. He saw us, but even when I had moved nearer and up the ridge a bit to flatten out my view of him, he was undisturbed. Now I could see his pale facial disks and knew him surely for an owl.

We stood for a long minute, mittened hands grasping the muzzles of our rifles, their butt-plates on the ground beside us. Only then did a dim, amateurish memory stir in me and I said to my wife, "I think that's a hawk owl."

A few moments later the bird casually left his perch, swept down towards the ground in a long graceful arc, then, at the proper function of a cyma curve, he swept up again and landed in the topmost branch of a lower tree. He paused a moment, then took off again, his wing beats as rapid as a falcon's; his flight, once he had decided on a further destination, was straight and arrow-swift. He disappeared around a small cluster of trees at the end of the nearby swamp.

A few miles of hiking and an hour of silent paddling in our canoe, and we were back at our camp. Without even waiting to light the gas lantern in the half-light, I moved into the dim interior, fumbled under my bunk for my duffel bag, and came up with Roger Tory Peterson's *A Field Guide to the Birds*. On page 133, I read:

A medium-sized, hawk-like day-flying owl (smaller than a crow), with a *long* falcon-like tail and *barred* underparts. At rest it maintains a more inclined body posture, not so upright as other owls; often perches at the tip-top of a tree or in some other exposed situation and jerks its tail in the manner of a sparrow hawk. Shrike-like it pitches from its perch, flies low and rises abruptly to its next perch . . .

Experts sometimes annoy one with their god-like expertise. It is only a temporary envy they stimulate, of course, for mostly they delight one by confirming that there is a real world, predictable, subject to confirmation in its many-sided phenomena, recognizable by the amateur observer. The lucky Mr. Peterson must have observed many hawk owls to enable him to extrapolate such essential data. He had precisely described and placed my hawk owl because "my" hawk owl was like his. And yours will be too when you are lucky enough to first see him.

This owl is well-named for his hawk-like qualities in addition to his characteristic perch. His long tail and his rapid wing beat, to say nothing of his falcon-pointed wings, remind one of the duck hawk in flight.

In west-central Labrador the spruce and muskeg swamp terrain provides an ideal habitat for hawk owls. I saw several perched in dead stubs along the Kepimits River in late June and early July of 1964. Once while strolling among the tepee-rings of a not-so-old Montagnais Indian camp, I came upon a hawk owl that refused to consider my intrusion. While I poked about the late domestic scene the owl ignored me. Later when I returned to collect wood for a noon fire, he let me go about my own domestic duties without showing any alarm at all, even though I passed directly under him a half dozen times. This owl ran true to his reputation for being bold, or as innocent as a "fool hen," for no one knows which trait explains his seeming fearlessness. I had several views of this hawk owl but it wasn't until I came back a second time for wood that I noticed a white-footed mouse held against the dead branch by a single talon. Finally I left this imperturbable owl to his own lunch, but I carried away with me a clear picture of the bird.

The hawk owl is a very dressy owl. He looks always as if he had on his best bib and tucker. He is neatly barred across his puffy breast and lower belly, and there are five or six much wider bars of two shades of dark gray brown across his long falcon-like tail. His facial disks are outlined clearly in black and his expression is intent, even business-like. There is nothing vacant or vague about his mien that one senses in some owls, nor is there quite the fierceness of the great horned owl's expression; certainly there is none of the absent-minded but thoughtful and rather intellectual look of the great gray owl. I think of the hawk owl as the efficiency expert among owls. He is used to facing up to things even in the harsh light of day.

My experiences with the hawk owl occurred in typical country for this bird, for one is not apt to encounter him in lower latitudes during the breeding season. He breeds in the northern parts of North America and is seen only rarely as far south as southern Ontario, Maine, the Dakotas, or southern British Columbia. He breeds as far north as Alaska and Arctic Canada and does not regularly migrate south.

My Kepimits hawk owl had caught his typical prey, for he is known as a mouser and a hunter of other small mammals. And he is a day-hunter, perhaps even more apt to be seen about his business in broad daylight than is the diurnal short-eared owl. Although those who have studied this owl consider his chief food to be mice, lemmings, ground squirrels and the like, in the late fall and winter the hawk owl is known to prey on ptarmigan. One observer saw a hawk owl with a weasel in his talons and it is said a hawk owl was known to have captured and flown off with a ruffled grouse. Food, as with most predaceous birds, is where he finds it.

THE LONG-EARED OWL

Once you find him—and there's the rub —the long-eared owl is one of the most interesting of all owls to observe. But he makes himself mighty scarce, and I once lived for two years in a house close to several long-eared owls without ever seeing one. This owl is very widely distributed throughout the country; indeed probably ninety percent of our population lives within twenty-five miles of one of these owls, yet few people ever see one. More oddly, this owl often roosts in small groups so when one is seen others are apt to be close by. I had seen this

owl as a boy in Indiana but I became acquainted with the bird, I might say, in Wayland, Massachusetts, when I discovered not one or two but six long-eared owls.

A heavily wooded deep ravine cut the area behind our house. A small stream ran through the flat, hardwood and evergreen bottoms, and parts of the ravine sides were real timbered thickets. While looking for the nest of a Cooper's hawk I had seen in the area, I had occasion to push my way through such a thicket of big and small hemlocks and white pines. Suddenly these slim, elongated owls were all around me. One I confronted almost face to face. As I stood at the top of the ravine, he was roosting almost at eye level, perched halfway up a pine that rose from the bottom of the ridge. I shall never forget him for as he compressed his

feathers and stretched upwards, he shrank visibly before my eyes until he seemed a beanpole of an owl. He looked more like the stub of a tree than a bird. There was another in the same tree and four more in two trees nearby. None offered to flush; all stretched and compressed themselves in the same manner and peered at me sleepily through slits made by half closing their eyes. The illusion of slimness is further accentuated in these birds by the placement of the long ear tufts. They are not located near the sides of the head, as is the case with the great horned owl, but are set close together near the center, and often stand straight up.

I searched out these owls on many occasions. I found their pellets; I located other roosting areas. Best of all, when the squirrel season opened and I regularly went out at

sunup to sit and watch and intercept the foraging squirrels when they left their den trees to come up the ridge for acorns, I saw these birds coursing the area on the hunt. Like all owls, save the pygmy, long-eared flies silently. On many mornings I would see one or two of these birds in bumpy, noiseless flight through these woods, looking more like big moths than birds. On some mornings before there was enough light to see the cross hairs of my .22 I watched for these owls and was quite often rewarded. Twice one of them alighted near me and bowed down from above as if to scrutinize and identify me. Although I never did see a long-eared owl make a kill, on one occasion one flew slowly by on its long wing carrying a mouse in the talons of one dangling leg. Small rodents make up eighty to ninety per-cent of the diet of this useful owl, but it does take infrequent small birds found in its habitat, such as warblers, or kinglets. On several evenings I saw this owl coursing over a field on the flat above the wooded area, but usually I encountered it in the wooded area itself.

The long-eared owl appears to be dark colored, his upper parts brown and quite variegated, with white and yellow brown mottling. Under his chin he shows some short dark vertical stripes, but his breast and belly are both striped and barred, giving a cross-hatched look. When his yellow eyes are open this owl has an angry look. The inner edges of the cinnamon colored facial disks just over his eyes is acutely outlined with an almost vertical V in white. On the outer edges these disks are bordered in black. His tail, longer

that than of most owls, is thinly and numer-ously barred.

Although I looked hard it was not until the third spring that I found this owl's nest. It was an old crow's nest in a white pine so high up that I was never able to see into it. I knew it for a long-eared's nest only when I flushed the bird on two or three occasions by clapping my hands and hallooing. Both times the owl flew off (usually it stayed put) and on neither occasion did the bird pull the "broken wing" act, so common to many birds, but practiced, it is said among owls, only by the long-eared owl. Once, the flushed owl snapped its beak sharply but uttered none of the mewing and whining that it sometimes resorts to when disturbed. In the spring, however, I heard these owls hooting their low oo-hooing call on a few occasions. This was in the early spring and to the best of my knowledge I never heard this owl later in the year, although at times, owing to the variety of calls owls make, I find myself confused in identifying positively the hoos of owls.

The long-eared owl is about the same size as his short-eared cousin but there the simi-larity ends. He is twelve and one half to six-teen inches in length and has a wingspread that appears greater than the three to three and a half feet it actually is, owing to the fact that this owl's wings are slender in compar-ison to those of other owls. Because of its long tail and long slender wings the long-eared owl actually appears larger in flight than he is. And when he pulls himself stiffly and thinly erect when disturbed on his perch he seems very long indeed.

THE VOICES OF THE OWLS

The cries of owls, which have drawn extravagant imitation from humans since time immemorial, are a paradox among sounds. They are intriguing because of their strange similarity to sounds made by the human voice, yet at the same time most of them defy human imitation. The literature of birds is filled with examples of men's attempts to render the hoot and wails phonetically. Men the world over have written the hoot of an owl with a "whoo" or "hoo" but that sound is virtually the only recorded owl call that brings forth uniform agreement. With that one easy syllable, agreement ends. The difficulty of consensus is revealed when one reads the myriad of descriptions and attempted phonetic imitations of the wild gabblings that mark, say, a barred owl's crazy cacophony. Man can call owls successfully by using the simple and character-istic whoo sequences of a particular species. Still Grant, a New Brunswick hunting guide (who was incidentally a fine moose caller), once tricked me into thinking I had tolled up a barred owl when in fact I was answering his own excellent imitations. But even this fine mimic could not reproduce that owl's mad laughter and wild gobblings. Not many birders would recognize as the same sound this owl's call as I carefully recorded it one afternoon in the Adirondacks when I was entertained by a barred owl's wild goings on. The sound I wrote down was rendered then (see chapter on barred owls) as "uh-*huh* wee ay *ouk.*" Reading the literature on owl calls is indeed a salutary experience, for the valiant efforts of students to imitate this bird's nonhooting calls are as varied as they are unsuccessful.

There are a number of perfectly understandable reasons for this, for the owl's calls produce as many verbal and written renderings as a Rorschach inkblot produces descriptive responses. We hear what we are conditioned to hear, and sometimes we are conditioned to hear the calls as others have previously recorded them. Sometimes we hear them as our own mood and tempers —our own characters—dictate we should. A wail that one person may find eerie, another may find merely comic. It all depends.

Most will agree that at times the lonely hoots of the owl are foreboding, portentous, even fearful. In an earlier chapter we saw how men built a folklore around this bird and seek to discover why, in describing owl calls, we are all influenced by it. Such descriptive words and phrases as "demoniacal laughter," "groans," "eerie and idiotic laughing calls," and "harsh, bloodcurdling screams" all hark back to the folklore, to other men's fears and attributions of the call of owls to things half-human and half-unworldly. When the birder records the owl's call as "goblin-like," for instance, he rings the same changes of of human response as Shakespeare did in *Macbeth*.

The owls themselves compound the difficulty, for the same species not only produces a number of variations on the basic call, but all owls utter many other squawks, hisses, screams, gobbles and chuckles that have nothing to do with the familiar identifying hoot. The barred owl's repertoire is a case in point. He does indeed deserve the name "eight hooter" for his hoo-hoo, hoo-hoo-hoo-hoo-hoo-hooaw" is basic and character-istic. But this owl also hoots variations on this call using a sometimes lesser number of hoots; worse, he has a veritable cacophony of other sounds that can make the same man who can identify his regular hoots think that another creature altogether must have produced the ungodly potpourri of decibels.

Just as most owl fanciers can identify, and even imitate successfully, the basic call of the barred owl, so they can usually identify and sometimes imitate (as my friend John Terres can) the five hoots of the great horned owl. The hoots of this grand bird once heard usually can be recognized on later occasions, for the profoundly deep resonance of these feathered bassos seems to originate inside the sounding bone of one's very skull rather than in the vocal chords of a creature scarcely bigger than a frying chicken.

We have contrasted the sonorous profundo of the great horned owl's five-toned call with the discreet, even staccato syllables of the barred owl's barking hoots. The latter's hoots seem the rebellious notes of the knave compared to those of the unchallenged authority of the king.

When the majesty of the horned owl is not at stake, he, too, can and does make a fine variety of less dignified sounds. A trapped owl I once observed not only snapped his beak angrily, but also made mean chuckling growling notes as well. Many people have attested to the great horned owl's screams, while others have referred to less fearful sounds made by this bird. Sometimes the long, drawn out hoooo-oo-ooo is almost a cooing note; on other occasions the whoo-hoo-oo-o

takes on a wavering tone similar (though greater in volume) to that of the screech owl. The horned owl's whoos are sometimes interspersed with a whah-what-wha-a-a-aw that has a quality of crazy laughter in it; on other occasions this owl makes a noise that some have described as a cat like meow or keow.

Arthur Bent has likened the carrying power of the five hoots of this owl to the "sound of a distant foghorn, or the far-away whistle" of an old steam locomotive. It is this call that most characterizes the great horned owl. Once heard, these five hoots are not easily forgotten.

In the chapter on barred owls I have tried to do justice to that bird's varied calls. He is surely one of the noisier owls of the wood.

The long-eared owl's call seems quite consistent with the shy, retiring nature of this recluse of the heavy thickets. He seems at times loath to over-advertise himself, and what I have heard and have surely identified as the calls of the long-eared owl are well described by one observer as "not harsh, but rather musical and mellow." The koo-koo-quoo notes of this owl are hooting sounds, to be sure, but come gently in the night. On occasions this owl, too, hoots in a low tremolo similar to that of the screech owl's characteristic waver.

But like his cousins the long-eared owl makes many other sounds, most of them, experts agree, during the mating season. He shrieks and screams on occasions, produces chirps and chuckles on others, makes long and short cat-like me-u-u-ews, and produces grunting and chuckling sounds not unlike "the barking of a small puppy," as C. W. Townsend noted fifty years ago. While this owl is versatile in voice, he is, for the most part, relatively silent, as unlikely to be heard casually as he is to be discovered in his thick cover.

When the short-eared owl is seen skimming the fields and marshes, one's first impression is that of easy motion and profound silence, but this owl has his repertoire. On one occasion I heard a short-eared owl produce a soothing, rather pre-occupied coo-cou sound while hunting. It was a sound that seemed almost an afterthought intended for himself alone. This owl seemed really to be talking to himself, without paying himself too much attention. It is said that the short-eared makes a variety of sounds during his spectacular courtship flight, sometimes squealing in an almost pig-like fashion, mixing this with a sneezing bark. He too, snaps his bill and hisses when intruded upon. Arthur Bent says that during migration and in winter, this owl is "one of the most silent of birds," but when the occasion calls for it, the short-eared owl can produce his share of strange owlish sounds.

When I was a small boy on the farm, my cousin and I always thought the barn owl was urging his mate or another owl on to violence. In flight this ghostly bird seemed to be saying sic-sic-sic-sic-sic, as we might have "sic-ed" the dog, Buster, on to some kind of action. The barn owl's high, discordant scream is indeed a terrifying sound, as are his growls and raspy rattling, the latter a sound he sometimes makes in flight. "Our" barn owl I heard scream only once, from the high, dark interior of my grandfather's hay mow. That one sound was enough for a boy after dark. I can still feel the hackles crawl from that one barn owl adventure.

My own associations with the screech owl's mournful call are recounted in chapter 4. Dr. Winsor M. Tyler's description impressed Arthur Bent, as it will all who have heard this little owl's strange quaver. He says:

> The commonest note of the screech owl is a whistle, well within human range, which, rising a little in pitch, becomes tremulous, then slides down below the starting point, the tremulous quality becoming so marked, that, near the end, the voice is almost divided into separate notes. The whole has a sad, dreary effect, due rather to the tone of the voice and the sliding change of pitch than to any minor intervals.
>
> The owl varies this cry in several ways. The note may begin on various pitches—that is, one wail may be markedly higher or lower than the wail preceding it; the pitch may rise very little, or it may rise two or more tones before it falls at the end; the pitch may fall a varying degree, sometimes three or four tones; and a fourth variation is at the beginning of the cry when the quavering quality is delayed appreciably.

Excellent as Dr. Tyler's description is, perhaps Thoreau has been most memorable in describing the screech owl's call, this one the bird's love call.

It is no honest *tu-whit, tu-who* of the poets, but, without jesting, a most solemn, graveyard ditty, the mutual consolations of suicide lovers remembering the pangs and the delights of supernal love in the infernal groves. *Oh-o-o-o-o that I had never been bor-r-r-r-n* sighs one on this side of the pond and circles with the restlessness of despair to some new perch on the gray oaks. Then—*that I had never been bor-r-r-r-n* echoes another on the further side with tremulous sincerity, and *bor-r-r-r-n* comes faintly from far in Lincoln woods.

During an Arctic summer's observation of a number of snowy owls, I did not hear one of them utter a sound. But my Eskimo friend, Kisik, assured me that they had a variety of calls. "Okpik scare you sometimes. He bark like sled dog sometimes; sometimes he make call like tu-lu-ok (raven)." Kisik, somewhat embarrassed, then volunteered, "He go like this sometimes *go-go-gok, go-go-gok*." Kisik sounded authentic, for no human can make such guttural sounds more deeply in his throat than an Eskimo. Bent, quoting Nuttal, gives another call as *whowh-whowh, hah, hah, hah*. Nuttal continues, "Other more dismal cries sound like the unearthly ban of Cerberus; and heard amidst a region of cheerless solitude, his lonely and terrified voice augments rather than relieves the horrors of the scene." Mr. Nuttal evidently found the Arctic prairie more forbidding than I did, although perhaps he saw it during the bleakness of winter, whereas my observations of the snowy owl took place when the tundra was bright.

In Part II of his *Life Histories of North American Birds of Prey*, Arthur Bent treats under the subtitle "Voice" the calls of all of the owls. This remarkable book, like all of this great ornithologist's books in the Smithsonian Institution's series, is not only a treasure trove of information on the voices of owls, but on the habits and life histories of the great birds as well. Every admirer of the owl should read it.

PYGMY OWL

SNOWY OWL

SCREECH OWL

BARN OWL

HAWK OWL

GREAT GRAY OWL

GREAT HORNED OWL

LONG-EARED OWL

SHORT-EARED OWL

BOREAL OWL

SAW WHET OWL

BURROWING OWL

BARRED OWL

ELF OWL

108

LIST OF OWLS

PYGMY OWL *(Glaucidium gnoma)*

The pygmy is a small, "earless" owl, noticeably tame, and common in coniferous and deciduous woods from the Rocky Mountains west to the Coast and from the Canadian border south into Mexico. It is about six inches in length, with a wingspread of fifteen inches. Its cocked black and white barred tail extends beyond the tips of its wings. This owl is rust colored, with white spots on the head, body, wings and upper flanks; the lower flanks are streaked with black. There is a black patch on the nape of its neck at each side. The pygmy owl nests in abandoned woodpecker holes, usually eight to twenty feet from the ground. It lays three or four white or whitish, nearly round eggs about one inch long. The pygmy owl flies with a very fast, most un-owl-like wing beat, with an undulating motion similar to that of a shrike.

SNOWY OWL *(Nyctea scandiaca)*

This is a large, "earless," white-appearing owl which is rarely all white. It is about twenty-five inches long, with a wingspread to sixty-six inches. Usually the back is mottled light brown on white; the underparts are sparsely barred with light brown on white. The facial disk is relatively small, and the beak appears to be "mustached." The female is much darker than the male, mottled and barred with a dark slate color. The snowy's voice is a hoarse *who who*, or it sometimes utters a growling bark or sharp whistle. It nests usually on the ground from northern Greenland and northern Alaska south through most of Canada. It lays five to eight eggs which are white or creamy white and roughly granulated. The snowy owl is an irregular migrant in winter to the northern United States, south as far as central Texas and east to South Carolina. On tundra it perches on frost heaves; in other areas near ground level.

SCREECH OWL *(Otus asio)*

The screech owl is a common small "eared" owl of towns, orchards and wood patches throughout the United States. It is about nine inches in length and has a wingspread of twenty-two inches. In the red phase, the upperparts are bright rufous, the underparts whitish, heavily mottled and streaked. Both sexes are alike. The screech owl's voice is a sad, quavering tremulo wail down the scale, or gentle, rapidly-repeated flute-like notes or barks on one pitch. It nests in cavities, woodpecker holes, and the like. The flammulated and whiskered owls of the American Southwest are similar and of the same genus. The screech owl usually lays five or six eggs which are pure white, oval, and moderately glossy.

BARN OWL *(Tyto alba)*

This is a large, long-legged, not too common owl. It ranges from the Canadian border to the Gulf of Mexico, except for mountainous areas. The barn owl inhabits old buildings, barns, steeples, and similar places. The upperparts are tawny yellow, mottled dusky; the lower parts are noticeably light-colored. Its face, white to yellow brown in color, is distinctly heart-shaped. It is fourteen to twenty inches in length and has a wingspread of forty-four inches. The sexes are alike. The voice is a weird, fearful hiss, a frightful scream or a series of clicks or querulous *aks*. The eggs are dead white, more pointed than usual for owls, and finely granulated. It usually lays from five to seven.

HAWK OWL *(Surnia ulula)*

A diurnal, "earless" owl of the muskeg and spruce swamp borders of northern Canada, the hawk owl perches in the open in the tips of treetops. A favorite perch is a dead spruce, where its angular, slantwise stance gives it a hawk-like appearance. It is fourteen to seventeen inches long, with a wingspread of thirty-three inches. Perched, this owl jerkily raises its long, barred tail and slowly lowers it. The flight is low and swift over marsh borders, undulating upwards as it comes to rest. In flight it often alternates flapping and gliding, and frequently it "treads air" and hovers in the manner of a sparrow hawk. The upperparts are mottled with dark, dusky brown; the lower parts are narrowly barred in brown and white. The facial disk is light gray, surrounded by black. The hawk owl nests in southern Canada and the extreme northern United States. This owl lays three to seven eggs, which are pure white and slightly glossy. The nest can be a mass of sticks and moss built in a tree twelve to fifteen feet from the ground, or eggs may be laid in hollows of dead tree stubs.

GREAT GRAY OWL *(Strix nebulosa)*

This owl of the far north appears to be the largest of all the North American owls. It is sometimes, but rarely, found in the mountainous, high elevations of the Sierra Nevada and Rockies, but prefers deep pine and spruce forests. This owl has a large, flat, round face, finely ringed in concentric circles in gray and brown; it is without ear tufts. The owl has yellow eyes. The upperparts are a dark, dusky brown mottled with small white areas, the underparts are grayish, strongly streaked with brown. It appears to have a black chin. The legs are heavily feathered and finely barred. The great gray owl is about twenty-two to thirty-three inches long, and has a wingspread of about sixty inches. The sexes look alike. It nests thirty to fifty feet from the ground, often in old hawks' nests built of twigs, well-cupped in shape and lined with bark strips and feathers. It lays two to five eggs, commonly three; they are dull white and roughly granulated, and seem small for the size of this owl.

GREAT HORNED OWL (Bubo virginianus)

This owl, one of the few large owls with ear tufts, is common throughout timbered regions in the United States and Canada to the very edges of the tundra. It has a conspicuously white throat collar above a heavily dark-streaked breast. The belly is heavily cross-barred, the back and wings are mottled brown. The eyes are yellow. It is usually twenty to twenty-three inches in length, and has a wingspread of nearly five feet. The sexes look alike, except that the female is usually larger. This owl appears singularly neckless and big-headed in flight, when the ear tufts do not show. It usually nests in large trees, thirty to seventy feet above the ground; the nest may be an old crow or red-tailed hawk nest or an old squirrel's nest, sometimes built in hollows or the broken apertures of trees. Usually the bird adds twigs and sticks and lines the nest with its own downy breast feathers. The great horned owl is an exceptionally early nester and is sometimes seen brooding its eggs (usually one to three) as early as February or even late January, even in the northern parts of its range. Owing to its large size, it is a ravenous generalized feeder, preying on rabbits, mice, rats, skunks, and birds of all kinds even large grouse and duck. Miscellaneous food includes snakes, fish, beetles, crawfish, grasshoppers, and an occasional housecat. The eggs are white and thick-shelled, showing little gloss, and are rough to the touch. There is an incubation period of twenty-eight to thirty days. This owl emits three to six deep, resonant hoots, and often five uninflected hoots in this pattern: *hoo, hoo-hoo, hoo, hoo.*

LONG-EARED OWL (Asio otus)

This owl prefers wooded areas close to open country. It ranges throughout the temperate zone of North America; it breeds in the northern half of the United States from California to southern Maine and southern Canada. It winters south as far as northern Texas and east to northern Georgia. It is a slender, brown gray owl, with ear tufts set relatively closer together and longer in proportion than those of the horned owl. The lower parts are buff and streaked lengthwise; the facial disks are a one-tone buff color, and rounder than those of the horned owl. This owl is sometimes confused with the horned owl, although it is much smaller, being about thirteen to fifteen inches long. With its forty inch wingspread, it has rather long wings for its size. The long-eared owl is even more exclusively nocturnal than certain other owls. Several may roost together in a thick, wooded area, and may allow an intruder to approach quite closely. It hides easily in an elongated perch on a limb near a tree bole. The long-eared seldom builds its own nest, often using that of a crow or other large bird. It may lay from three to eight eggs, but four or five is most common; the incubation period is twenty-one days. This owl takes small- and medium-sized birds as prey, especially during the period when it is feeding its young, but during most of the year its food consists mainly of mice, rats, chipmunks, and other small rodents. Like most owls, the long-eared makes a variety of sounds and calls, but its common call is either a soft, mellow, dove-like *quoo-quoo-quoo*, or a long, low *quo-oo-oo.*

SHORT-EARED OWL (Asio flammeus)

This is the owl of the open fields, plains, sloughs, and marshes, the coursing owl that hunts by day over the same terrain, often, that the marsh hawk or harrier patrols. It flops in a slovenly and irregular way over the open areas, appearing (between its long glides) as a huge, moth-like creature. Buff beneath, (and unevenly streaked on its lower parts) it appears light-colored, short-necked, and big-headed to the observer. The upper parts are brownish and also heavily streaked, with a dark, near-black crescent near the bend of the underwing. Its ear tufts are short and hard to see, and its eyes have a dark ring around them, giving the bird a dissipated look. In its nesting or wintering range it is found over all of North America from Mexico to the northernmost edge of the tundra. It is thirteen to seventeen inches long, and has long, tapering and rather pointed wings (a forty-one inch spread) when seen in flight. It nests on the ground using local grasses, weed stalks, and feathers. The short-eared owl takes birds on occasion but its prey is made up mostly of mice, voles and lemmings. The eggs, which are creamy white, number five or six, and the incubation period is about twenty-one days. This owl is one of the most silent of birds except during courtship, when it utters a variety of clucks, barks, and squealing sounds.

BOREAL OWL (Aegolius funereus)

This rich chocolate brown owl of the far north, sometimes known as Richardson's owl, is about the size of the screech owl. It shows a gray facial disk framed with a black border. Its back is white-spotted; the spots on its forehead are smaller and finer than those on the back. The boreal owl shows a brown-streaked breast and has a wingspread of about two feet. This little owl seems inordinately tame when encountered in the daytime and presents a heavy-lidded, sleepy look to the observer. It nests in old woodpecker holes or natural cavities right to the northern edge of timber and is occasionally seen in winter in the United States border states and northern New England. The boreal owl is mostly a mouse feeder, although it probably occasionally takes small birds and evidently often feeds on beetles and other such insects. Like most owls the boreal is capable of a variety of sounds. Both white and Indian observers have noted that one call sounds like water dripping. The Montagnais Indians' name for this owl means "water dropping bird."

SAW WHET OWL (Aegolius acadica)

This little owl, smaller than a screech owl, is more apt to be heard than seen, at least during its breeding season, for it is one of the most retiring of all the owls. When it is heard it may be identified either by the low, mellow, and endlessly repeated (often over one hundred times) whistle, *too, too, too, too;* or by the metallic whistle that gives the bird its name, a sound resembling the filing or whetting of a saw. This cinnamon brown bird (spotted and splotched above with white) shows a white breast heavily streaked with a few wide, brown stripes. Its facial disk displays a kind of sunburst of fine brownish streaks radiating away from the yellow eyes. Generally a coniferous woods bird, the earless little saw whet nests usually in tree cavities, from central and southern Canada into the United States, and winters as far south as southern California and the northern edges of the Gulf states. Mice, shrews, bats, young red squirrels, and flying squirrels comprise most of the prey. It lays four to seven white, oval—sometimes almost globular—eggs.

BURROWING OWL *(Speotyto cunicularia)*

This small, sand-colored owl of the prairies is tuftless and long-legged. It is often seen in the daytime either perched on the ground or a fence post. This owl lives in holes, and was formerly a common occupant of prairie dog towns, where it could be seen bobbing and bouncing in agitation as it does when disturbed. The upperparts of the burrowing owl are light brown buff, spotted with large white spots on the back and finer ones over the forehead and top of head. The underparts are barred in a lighter buff color. This round-headed owl is a voracious feeder on mice and a wide variety of insects; indeed, it is a most generalized feeder taking some small birds (especially while feeding its brood), young prairie dogs, pocket gophers, lizards, scorpions, and all varieties of mice. While the burrowing owl uses the holes of prairie dogs and ground squirrels, it is perfectly capable of enlarging and cleaning out old nests. Oddly enough, the lining of the nests, often consists of dried cattle droppings, finely chipped. It lays six to eleven eggs which are rather round and glossier than most owl eggs. The most common note of this owl is a tremulous chattering chuckle. At night the burrowing owl makes a high and mellow *coo-coo-hoo*. Its range includes the western United States and Mexico.

ELF OWL *(Micrathene whitneyi)*

This *sparrow-sized* owl is the smallest of our owls. In its tiny range (southern Arizona, southwestern New Mexico, Sonora and extreme southeastern California) where its favorite haunt, the saguaro cactus, thrives, it is fairly abundant, taking over for nesting sites holes made by woodpeckers and flickers. It is about six inches in length, with a fifteen inch wingspread. Round-headed and short-tailed, this elfin bird shows an indistinctly streaked breast, tiny spots on its forehead, and a light brown back not heavily splotched with white except along the top of its wings. The elf owl seems to be primarily an insect feeder, taking crickets, grass-hoppers, caterpillars, and centipedes. It is nocturnal in its habits but may be observed or heard at dusk, uttering its mix of squeaks, churrs, cackles, and *churps*. It lays from three to five eggs (usually three).

FERRUGINOUS OWL *(Glaucidium brasilianum)*

This owl, formerly known as the ferruginous pygmy owl, is indeed a close relative of the pygmy, but inhabits a very restricted range, a narrow strip of the extreme southwestern United States in Arizona and an equally narrow strip on the lower Rio Grande River. The ferruginous owl can be told from its close relative by its unspotted back and the faint black barring on its rather long tail (as contrasted with the white barring on the tail of Glaucidium gnoma.) It is about six inches in length, the wingspread is fifteen inches. It lays three to four eggs, often in old woodpecker holes in cotton-woods or mesquites. The food of this little owl includes mice, small birds, and insects.

WHISKERED OWL *(Otus trichopsis)*

This "eared" owl, formerly known as the spotted screech owl, has been found to be a separate species and not a sub-species. Like its relatives it has a gray and a red phase, that is, it is dichromatic. It is found in a tiny section of Arizona, and the Huachuca Mountains and ranges on down into Mexico. The barks of this owl are generally repeated six times in rapid succession and the sound has been written as *boot-boot-boot-boot-boot-boot*. It is largely an insect eater. The length is six and one half inches; the wingspread sixteen inches. The owl lays three or four white eggs, usually in old woodpecker holes.

FLAMMULATED OWL *(Otus flammeolus)*

This member of the genus, *Otus*, inhabits the Rocky Mountain states. It is slightly smaller than the common screech owl, and like its near relative, occurs in the gray and rusty phases. In a section of southeast Arizona the three representatives of *Otus*, the screech owl, the whiskered, and the flamminated, occur together. While this species has ear tufts, they tend to be rounded and not as noticeable as those of the screech owl. This bird is mostly insectivorous. Three or four white, slightly glossy eggs are laid in an old wood-pecker's hole.

BARRED OWL *(Strix varia)*

This is a large, earless, brownish gray owl with a large, puffy head and dark soulful eyes. Its "goitered" neck and upper breast are finely barred crosswise and its belly is coarsely streaked lengthwise on a light, buff background. Its brown back is spotted with white. Known as the "eight hooter," its call is sometimes written as "Who cooks for you? Who cooks for you-all?" But the barred owl makes a fantastic variety of other catcalls, barks, squalls, and cater-wauling that can raise the hackles of any listener. This is the owl of the southern swamps and the deep moist woods of of the north. Its range consists of southern Canada and all of the United States east of the Rockies. The barred owl is a big owl (sixteen to twenty-two inches in length), larger than a barn owl, but smaller than a great horned. Its broad wings reach a spread of nearly four feet. The food of the barred owl is quite generalized, partly because of the bird's relatively large size. The owl is a great mouser, but also takes rats, chipmunks, red, gray, and flying squirrels, as well as rabbits and young hares. In addition, it takes a variety of birds from grouse to warblers in size; also frogs, salamanders, small snakes; and a variety of insects. This owl likes heavy pine woods for nesting and often takes over an old nest of a hawk or other large bird. But the barred owl will also nest in tree cavities, laying its two to three eggs right on the wood chips.

SPOTTED OWL *(Strix occidentalis)*

This is the rather rare western counterpart of the barred owl. It ranges along the coast from lower British Colombia to lower California and east across southern Arizona and New Mexico. Unlike that of the barred, this owl's breast is finely and horizontally barred.